D0490804

Beauty Therapy
Practical Skills for NVQ 3

The Learning Centre
Abingdon College
Northcourt Road
Abingdon
Oxon
OX14 1NN
Tel: 01235 216240

646 72
fr?.

Beauty Therapy
Practical Skills for NVQ 3

FRANCES FRANKLIN and BOB WOODHOUSE

Contributing authors:

Troy Roberts (Aromatherapy massage)
Angela Wheat (Electro-epilation)
Denise Wright (Nail treatments)

In association with
City & Guilds

Hodder & Stoughton
A MEMBER OF THE HODDER HEADLINE GROUP

646.72
FRA

Orders: please contact Bookpoint Ltd, 78 Milton Park, Abingdon, Oxon OX14 4TD. Telephone: (44) 01235 827720, Fax: (44) 01235 400454. Lines are open from 9.00 – 6.00, Monday to Saturday, with a 24 hour message answering service. Email address: orders@bookpoint.co.uk

British Library Cataloguing in Publication Data
A catalogue record for this title is available from The British Library

ISBN 0 340 773022

First published 2000
Impression number   10 9 8 7 6 5 4 3 2 1
Year   2005 2004 2003 2002 2001 2000

Copyright © 2000 Bob Woodhouse and Frances Franklin

All rights reserved. No part of this publication may be reproduced or transmitted in any form or by any means, electronic or mechanical, including photography, recording, or any information storage and retrieval system without permission in writing from the publisher or under licence from the Copyright Licensing Agency Limited. Further details of such licences (for reprographic reproduction) may be obtained from the Copyright Licensing Agency Limited, of 90 Tottenham Court Road, London W1P 9HE.

Cover photo from Telegraph Colour Library: Photographer Michel Kramer

Illustration and page make-up by Jordan Publishing Design, Salisbury, Wiltshire

Printed in Italy for Hodder & Stoughton Educational, a division of Hodder Headline Plc, 338 Euston Road, London NW1 3BH by Printer Trento Srl

Contents

Acknowledgements   7

Introduction   9

     About this book   9

     National standards   10

     How to use this book   11

     Chapter/element cross reference guide   14

1 Beauty therapy industry

     Contents   17

     Introduction   18

     Career opportunities in beauty therapy   18

     Personal career action plan   23

2 Client care and consultation

     Contents   26

     Introduction   27

     Responding to your client   27

     Pre-treatment assessment   29

     Feedback   31

     Summary   32

     Further study   33

     Review questions   33

3 Effective working practices

     Contents   34

     Introduction   35

     Projecting the image   35

     Efficient working practices   35

     Maintaining services and operations   38

     Sales   41

     Making the sale   42

     Consumer legislation (Law)   44

     Summary   45

     Further study   45

     Review questions   46

4 Working safely

Contents   47

Introduction   48

Legislation (Law)   48

Maintaining a safe working environment   50

Handling stock   52

Your professional appearance   54

Instruments and equipment   56

Working with your clients   59

Salon security   61

Summary   63

Further study   63

Review questions   64

5 Facial treatments

Contents   65

Introduction   66

Preparing a treatment plan   66

Vapour treatment   66

High frequency   68

Vacuum suction   71

Galvanism   74

Faradic type treatment   76

Microcurrent   78

Summary   79

Further study   79

Review questions   80

6 Figure diagnostics

Contents   81

Introduction   82

Providing advice on dietary control   83

Figure diagnosis   85

Posture   89

Fitness   94

Summary   102

Further study   102

Review questions   103

7 Body massage

Contents 104

Preparation 105

Main massage movements 106

Massage routine 108

Completion of treatment 112

Summary 113

Further study 113

Review questions 113

8 Body treatments

Contents 114

Preliminary consultation 115

Skin sensitivity tests 115

Gyratory vibrator 116

Audio sound 118

Percussion 118

Vacuum suction 119

Galvanic 121

Faradic type treatment 122

Summary 126

Further study 126

Review questions 127

9 Electro-epilation

Contents 128

Introduction 129

Hair 129

Temporary methods of hair removal 134

Electrolysis 135

Electro-epilation 135

Methods of electro-epilation 137

Contra-indications to electro-epilation 142

Needles 143

Re-growth hair 145

Summary 146

Further study 147

Review questions 147

10 Aromatherapy

Contents	148
Introduction	149
Essential oils	149
Unsafe oils and precautions	151
How oils work	153
Choosing oils for your client	157
Applying aromatherapy massage	161
Evaluating your treatment	163
Summary	164
Further study	165
Review questions	165

11 Specialist make up

Contents	166
Introduction	167
Patients and consultation	167
Treatment work area	169
Camouflage technique	170
Corrective technique	173
Aftercare	178
Summary	178
Further study	178
Review questions	179

12 Artificial nail techniques

Contents	180
Introduction	181
Anatomy and physiology	181
Disorders and diseases of the nail	184
Introduction to nail extensions	186
Tips and overlay	187
Acrylic nails	188
Fibre glass nails	191
Gel nails	194
Aftercare	196
Summary	196
Further study	196
Review questions	197

13 Heat treatments

Contents   198

Heat treatments   199

Sauna   200

Steam treatment   201

Spa pool   203

Paraffin wax   203

Infra-red light   205

Summary   205

Further study   206

Review questions   206

14 Ultra violet tanning treatments

Contents   207

Ultra-violet radiation   208

Basic safety rules   210

Summary   211

Further study   211

Review questions   211

15 Model answers   213

16 Your personal skill check   221

Index   229

Acknowledgements

The following photographs were taken at Croydon College by David Sparrow, under the technical direction of Bob Woodhouse and Frances Franklin:

Figures
1.1 to 1.8
2.1 to 2.3
3.1 to 3.6
4.3, 4.5
5.1 to 5.3
6.3 to 6.5, 6.10 to 6.18, 6.21 to 6.26
7.1
8.1 to 8.3, 8.5, 8.9 to 8.14
9.5 to 9.7
10.3 to 10.6, 10.8 to 10.9
12.4, 12.6, 12.14 to 12.21
13.2, 13.4

The authors and publishers would like to record their gratitude to Croydon College Marketing Department and the staff of the Hairdressing and Beauty Therapy Departments for the use of their Peppermint Studio facilities. In particular they would like to thank Suzanne Cullum, Yvette Swales and Melanie Farlow for their invaluable support and technical expertise.

Make-up and technical support for photographs in Chapter 11 by Jo Cater.

Nail treatments and technical support for photographs in Chapter 12 by Denise Wright.

Models: Sitadevi Chooramun, Chris Daldy, Justine Daldy, Julie Eames, Melanie Farlow, Ria Hernandez, Shirley King, Louisa Poole, Yvette Swales.

The authors and publishers are grateful to Science Photo Library for permission to reproduce Figures 13.1 to 13.4.

Photographs on pages 79, 201 and 204 were supplied by E.A. Ellison and Co. Limited, and those on pages 208 and 211 by Tansun Ltd.

Introduction

ABOUT THIS BOOK

To the student

This book will provide you with the guidance required to help you acquire the skills necessary to become a professional beauty therapist. Included is the required knowledge, or guidance in its acquisition, needed to achieve the current National Vocational Qualification or Scottish Vocational Qualification (NVQ or SVQ) at Level 3. In each chapter you will be provided with information and instructions on how to acquire practical skills. A combination of colour and black and white illustrations will help you to understand the practical tasks. Each chapter includes further study directives to help you obtain the relevant knowledge and understanding as well as questions to test yourself (with model answers in chapter 15) and to check your learning.

You may use the whole of this book, or you may follow those sections which apply to your current needs, at the appropriate level. On pages 221 to 228 is a 'personal skill check' that you may use to identify your existing skills and to direct yourself to those areas that require development. The skill check may be copied for your personal use to chart your progress, and will provide you with evidence of your professional development in your job role.

To the trainer/lecturer

This book is designed to support the emerging beauty therapist and may be used as a support to a structured programme of delivery, both as a course textbook and as a reference text. It will facilitate the flexible candidate-centred ethos of Vocational Qualifications by enabling those whose preferred style of learning is self-supported study to work at their own pace, providing the necessary knowledge or direction in obtaining this through flexible learning centres. This book will enable the student to achieve a basic grasp of these skills. For those candidates who follow a more formalised style of directed learning, this book provides reference points as well as both visual and text direction in how to carry out beauty therapy tasks. The book takes a holistic view of the beauty therapy industry and provides the student with this perspective of the industry.

The Personal Skill Check (see pages 221 to 228) may be used by the candidate to identify any previously acquired learning and to chart and review progress towards developing skills and understanding. It may prove a useful tool within the advice and guidance stages of student induction. This chapter may be photocopied for multiple use by the owner of this book.

NATIONAL STANDARDS

A government report 'Education and training working together' (1985) resulted in the introduction of National Vocational Qualifications and Scottish Vocational Qualifications. These qualifications are based on National Standards of competence that are relevant to a particular industry or sector.

National Standards for Beauty Therapy indicate the standard of competent performance, knowledge and understanding that is expected of someone working within beauty therapy. To ensure that these National Standards remain relevant to the industry that they serve, they are reviewed regularly.

NATIONAL TRAINING ORGANISATIONS

As the Industry Training Organisation for beauty therapy, the Beauty Industry Authority (BIA) has the responsibility for developing training for beauty therapy. The Beauty Industry Authority is part of the National Training Organisation (NTO) Hairdressing and Beauty Industry Authority (HABIA). NTO's have a strategic role in identifying current and future skill needs and assuring that arrangements are in place for meeting those skill needs. The authors acknowledge the role and contribution that the NTO has played in these standards.

ACHIEVING NVQ OR SVQ

NVQs and SVQs are achieved by demonstrating that you are competent within your job role and that you have the knowledge and understanding of the principles and practices which underpin these skills. The National Standards define what the job role is; they determine which tasks are normally undertaken by a person within that role (units) and then separate each task into its component stages (elements). Each element describes an activity that is judged against performance criteria; that is, how someone should carry out that activity. It may be necessary to prove competence within the activity in a range of situations or variables.

Competence is the ability to undertake a task to the standards which are expected of that industry.

To prove competence, knowledge and understanding against these National Standards you must produce evidence; that is, something that proves you can do what you claim. The most effective way of providing such proof is to undertake the activity within a real client–therapist situation and this can be observed by a qualified assessor who is also a competent therapist. This is by far the most effective method of proving competence. For limited areas it may be possible to simulate a real event, in place of an actual client–therapist activity. This can be done when demonstrating competence in areas which rarely occur or in which when they do occur there is an element of risk.

It is not always possible for an assessor to observe every task within all the variables required and in those cases it may be necessary for you to provide alternative evidence of your performance for assessment by the assessor. These alternatives may include your personal statement or description of the process undertaken, actual forms/record cards completed by you, testimony by others (possibly your client, a colleague, an employer or supervisor), or projects or assignments which are a collection of various forms of evidence. If you have existing beauty therapy or other relevant qualifications, or have undertaken previous training or have previous relevant experience it may be possible to present this as evidence. Any evidence must prove competence that is current and must be relevant to the National Standards being proven.

In some cases, when it has not been appropriate to demonstrate competence through your own performance, whether it is observed by an assessor or not, competence may be proven by producing evidence of potential capability.

Records of assessment and other evidence being used to prove competence, knowledge and understanding are presented, for certification, in the form of a portfolio. This is the collection of evidence, indexed and cross-referenced to the National Standards.

Note. Those who wish to pursue an NVQ or SVQ are recommended to discuss and plan their evidence collection and presentation with their assessor, each awarding body and assessment centre will have their own specific requirements, though all will work within the same National Standards framework.

As a candidate working towards the achievement of a National/Scottish Vocational Qualification it is your responsibility to present evidence assessment. When you consider yourself ready for assessment you should discuss this with your allocated assessor. Your assessor will support you in determining if you are ready for a formative or summative assessment.

You will be guided towards the suitability of forms of evidence and/or tasks undertaken in relation to the Units/Elements that you wish to achieve. With your assessor you will agree a plan for assessment that will confirm: the evidence to be presented; the task to be undertaken which the evidence will confirm; the elements of the NVQ/SVQ against which the evidence will be judged; the timescale for the assessment; agreed review dates.

During this planning process you should feel free to contribute your thoughts regarding how you will prove your competence. Each assessment centre will have procedures to follow if agreement cannot be made.

Remember – it is your role to present evidence of competence - your assessor will provide you with support, guidance and encouragement to undertake this in a manner that is acceptable to the Awarding Body.

> **TIP: Formative Assessment –** assessment undertaken while you are developing skills to confirm competent practice and identify areas for development.
>
> **Summative Assessment –** assessment undertaken when you are fully competent and it is anticipated that this will be confirmed via the assessment process.

HOW TO USE THIS BOOK

This book is divided into chapters, thirteen of which focus specifically on the requirements for the NVQ/SVQ at level 3 for beauty therapy. Each chapter focuses on a particular skill, task or aspect of this industry. You may read this book starting from the beginning or you may use it as a source of essential knowledge and a training manual by locating the particular skill you require, either through the index or by using the following grid, which indicates what elements are addressed by each chapter.

The main topics of each chapter of the book are listed in the left hand column and to the side you will find the cross referencing to the elements included within the chapter.

You will find that the related areas of, for example, health and safety or client consultation are clustered together within their own chapter and then the technical skills, for example waxing, are referenced to them when appropriate.

The review questions will enable you to produce evidence of your competence in the areas of knowledge and understanding and the further study will direct you towards the additional knowledge you require and often help you to produce evidence of this. The model answers contained within chapter 15 are there to confirm correct responses and to provide you with feedback. Use them wisely, and remember that you only fool yourself if you claim to be more knowledgeable than you really are. Model answers are best used to confirm correct responses, not as a means to quick learning, as they cover only a limited range of the knowledge requirement.

Your Personal Skill Check, on pages 221 to 228 will enable you to review your progress from the beginning of your programme of study through to achievement of your chosen award. You may make copies of pages 221 to 228 for your own use, so that you may review your progress regularly. This will not only help you to identify your existing competence and when you are ready for assessment, but also to identify where you still need practice and where you need training. This Skill Check will also prompt you to identify how you can prove your competence in a particular skill.

CHAPTER/ELEMENT CROSS REFERENCE GUIDE

Introduction

1 Beauty therapy industry		Level 3

2 Client care and consultation		11.1 Provide consultation 11.2 Advise on and promote services and products to clients 11.3 Gain feedback from clients to improve services

3 Effective working practices		11.1 Provide individual consultation services 11.2 Advise on and provide services and products to clients 11.3 Gain feedback from clients charts to improve services 12.1 Contribute to the effective use of resources 12.2 Contribute to effective productivity within the salon 13.1 Maintain safe working practices within the salon

4 Working safely		12.1 Contribute to the effective use of resources 13.1 Maintain safe working practices within the salon 13.2 Monitor and maintain salon security 18.2 Prepare the work area and client for the application of make up

5 Facial electrical		14.1 Assess clients and prepare treatment plans 14.2 Prepare the treatment room and client for electrical treatments 14.3 Treat clients using electrical equipment 13.1 Maintain safe working practices within the salon 11.1 Provide individual consultation services

6 Figure diagnosis	
	11.1 Provide individual consultation services
	14.1 Assess clients and prepare treatment plans
	15.1 Assess clients for body massage
	17.1 Assess clients and prepare treatment plans

7 Body massage	
	15.1 Assess clients for body massage
	15.2 Prepare the treatment room and client for body massage
	15.3 Massage the body to meet client requirements

8 Body treatment	
	14.1 Assess clients and prepare treatment plans
	14.2 Prepare the treatment room and client for mechanical and electrical treatments
	14.3 Treat clients using mechanical and electrical equipment

9 Electo-epilation	
	16a.1 Assess clients and prepare treatment plans
	16a.2 Prepare the treatment room and client for epilation
	16a.3 Carry out diathermy and blend epilation to meet the treatment plan
	16b.1 Assess clients and prepare treatment plans
	16b.2 Prepare the treatment room and client for epilation
	16b.3 Carry out diathermy and galvanic epilation to meet the treatment plan

10 Aromatherapy	
	17.1 Assess clients and prepare treatment plans
	17.2 Prepare for aromatherapy body massage
	17.3 Massage the body using aromatherapy techniques
	17.4 Gain feed back from clients and advice on aftercare

11 Specialist make up

18.1 Assess clients and prepare treatment plans

18.2 Prepare the work area and client for the application of make up

18.3 Apply make up using specialist techniques

18.4 Advise on self application and aftercare

12 Artificial nails

19.1 Assess clients and prepare treatment plans

19.2 Prepare the work area and client for the application of artificial nail structures

19.3 Apply artificial nail structures to meet client requirements

19.4 Maintain artificial nail structures

13 Heat treatments

20.1 Advise on dry and wet heat treatments

20.2 Prepare for dry and wet heat treatments

20.3 Monitor dry and wet heat treatments

13.1 Maintain safe working practices within the salon

14 Ultra violet tanning treatments

21.1 Advise clients on UV tanning

21.2 Prepare the treatment area and client for UV tanning

21.3 Monitor UV tanning sessions

15 Model answers

16 Your personal skill check

1 Beauty therapy industry

This chapter will provide you with guidance about the range of career opportunities in the beauty therapy sector. You will find that some roles are quite similar in their working environment while others are quite diverse and give considerable variation. It is this variation that makes beauty therapy such an interesting career for a wide range of people, who all enjoy close working relationships with others.

CONTENTS

Introduction   18

Career opportunities in beauty therapy   18

Personal career action plan   23

INTRODUCTION

This profession supplies a wide range of services to members of the public. As an international profession, beauty therapy provides the opportunity to travel and work throughout the world in a wide variety of formats. The skills required of the beauty therapist are respected as those of a technical nature. Members of the public are becoming more appreciative of the skills necessary to give a level of safe service in the relevant legislative framework. They now look to the achievement of recognised qualifications by those who provide them with treatment. Use the information and suggestions in this chapter to help plan your career progression. There is a career action plan in the summary of this chapter; use this to help you plan your professional career.

In the beauty therapy profession there are a number of differing service aspects, providing you with the opportunity to specialise in areas which are primarily:

- therapeutic – relaxing massage
- corrective – exercise, alternative therapy
- cosmetic – hair removal
- retail – sale of homecare products.

This range gives the beauty therapist career opportunities that can develop from one area to another; for example, to move into certain areas of work there are pre-requisites of existing skills and qualifications. It can be possible to cluster a number of different service aspects or to specialise. While, in most cases, qualifications for technical skills are not required by legislation, to obtain professional liability insurance qualification is often a pre-requisite. Some local authorities require the registration of premises, which often calls for the demonstration of competence. This is usually achieved by gaining qualifications. It is important that as a professional the therapist keeps up to date with recent technical developments so that relevant advice and guidance can be offered to clients.

Activity in the beauty therapy sector may be undertaken in a wide range of locations, including high street beauty salons, in-store beauty salons, hotel beauty salons, airports, health farms, medical centres, leisure centres and spas, the home, training centres and colleges.

CAREER OPPORTUNITIES IN BEAUTY THERAPY

Beauty therapist

Beauty therapists have a high level of professional competence across a very wide range of vocational skills. Their role provides possibly the widest range of employment opportunity in as many locations. While working as part of a team, the beauty therapist usually operates on a one to one basis with the client. The therapist must be able to manage her own working time and be well organised. She must also enjoy working with people and have good interpersonal and communication skills.

A recognised beauty therapy qualification is required by the industry before anyone is able to practise in this role. The beauty therapist often provides a wide range of services and must be able to move from one treatment range to another with ease. In some larger beauty salons it is not unusual for the therapist to specialise in a particular service area.

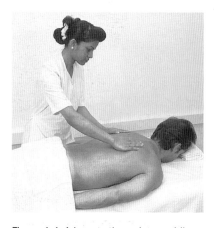

Figure 1.1 A beauty therapist providing a massage

Salary often includes a performance-related aspect that is determined by how much business is undertaken (commission) along with a basic level of payment.

Beautician

The beautician is a specialist who provides facial treatments and hand, arm and feet treatments. The beautician may offer this service in a beauty therapy salon, health farm, or department store (as part of the retail section). For those with a professional interest in beauty therapy, but not with regard to the torso of the body, this career forms a viable route. It is also a role that may be taken up during the earlier phases of the beauty therapist's training. The beautician will require not only good vocational skills, but also communication and some artistic skills.

The beautician's salary structure may differ between organisations but usually has an element of performance-related payment.

The skills of the beautician are often transferable to the areas of a remedial camouflage and theatrical and media make up, though both of these areas do require considerable additional skills.

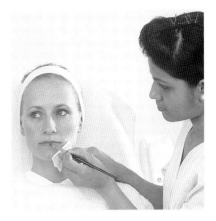

Figure 1.2 Artistic skills are important to the beautician

Electrologist

This is a highly specialised role in which some fully qualified beauty therapists decide to specialise. It requires the same skills needed for beauty therapy. Due to the nature of this treatment the electrologist must be fully qualified to satisfy insurance requirements as well as health and safety. Good interpersonal and communication skills are necessary for this role.

Salary often includes a performance-related aspect along with a basic level of payment.

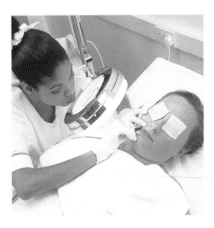

Figure 1.3 Electrology is a highly specialised skill

Holistic therapist

There are numerous complementary therapies, many having a high profile today. Some therapies have a beauty therapy focus while others have a more medical focus. Care must be taken in selecting the route which will provide the relevant foundation for the focus you have elected. For all therapies a thorough understanding of human anatomy and physiology is needed, and in many cases a knowledge and skill in massage can be supportive. For most complementary therapies a formal vocational qualification is recommended. Good communication and interpersonal skills are desirable in this role as it involves much personal one to one contact.

Employment may be as a consultant providing a service in a clinic or by home visiting.

Aromatherapist

As for the complementary therapist, the aroma therapist may pursue a beauty therapy or a quasi-clinical career pathway. This service is normally provided in a beauty therapy salon, health farm or clinic. The therapist usually uses aromatherapy oils combined with massage. The therapist must be skilled in this area as essential oils may be dangerous if used incorrectly. A relevant vocational qualification is recommended and the prior achievement of qualifications including body massage can be advantageous for this career. Good communication and interpersonal skills are desirable due to the high level of one to one contact.

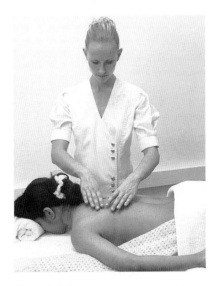

Figure 1.4 An aromatherapist combines a knowledge of aromatherapy oils with massage skills

The salary is often linked with a performance-related aspect, with a commission based upon income generated through your work activity.

Remedial camouflage

The masking of non required skin features is an area of employment for those with make up skills. Hospitals and skin specialist clinics often employ therapists to reduce the appearance of skin blemishes that may be the result of congenital disorder, accidents or surgery.

For those who enjoy working with a clinical environment as a specialist within a team of diverse specialisms, this can be a rewarding activity. The remedial camouflage specialist will often work with patients who are under considerable stress and are seeking support.

Beauty consultant

The consultant is a specialist who provides guidance and advice to clients on their choice and use of homecare products as well as professional beauty therapy treatments. This role is often combined with that of either a beautician, therapist or sales person.

The consultant will have a wide knowledge of the treatments or products for which they provide guidance. Good interpersonal and communication skills are required for this role as it involves much one to one contact.

The consultant's salary structure may differ between organisations but usually has an element of performance-related payment.

Demonstrator

This role frequently entails considerable travel and time away from home. It may involve demonstrating in stores and shops, at exhibitions or in beauty salons. Demonstrations may be presented to consumers, introducing them to products and homecare equipment, as is often the case in stores and shops. The demonstrator will attract the audience and hold their attention while they introduce and demonstrate the product.

When demonstrating professional products, the service may be a response to a salon owner's request or in a professional beauty therapy related exhibition. The audience will probably be knowledgeable and have made a conscious decision to attend.

The demonstrator may be a fully qualified beauty therapist or may be trained just in the use of the particular product being promoted. They may be employed by a product equipment manufacturer to promote their own specific ranges, by a wholesaler promoting a range of manufacturer's products that are sold by them, or by a marketing company to promote a specific product at a particular event or series of events.

Salary is often determined by the level of activity either individually or collectively as a promotional team. Employment may be on a regular basis or occasionally on demand.

Exercise trainer

Usually working in a health farm or fitness centre, the exercise trainer provides guidance in exercise regimes which are appropriate for the individual. This work is normally undertaken with groups of clients rather than on a one to one basis, though in some centres this may be the case. Styles of exercise evolve and change it is therefore important that up-to-date skills are maintained.

Figure 1.5 Beauty consultants need a wide knowledge of products and good communication skills

Figure 1.6 An exercise trainer needs to be a communicator and a motivator

Communication and motivational skills are necessary for this role as well as the relevant vocational qualifications. This may be a role that a beauty therapist pursues or it can be undertaken by a person who has the relevant qualification but is not a therapist.

Manicurist/Pedicurist

This role is often performed by the beauty therapist in the early stages of professional development. This area of work can become a career in itself or part of the progression through beauty therapy. The manicurist/pedicurist may provide this service in a beauty therapy salon, health farm, hairdressing salon, nail specialist's salon (a recent introduction in many shopping centres) or as a home visiting service.

The ranges of specialised artificial nails applications have introduced the role of the specialised nail application and nail decoration artist. The manicurist/pedicurist often specialises with a particular product range.

Good communication/customer service skills as well as the relevant technical skills are required for this job. The manicurist/pedicurist's salary is often supplemented by commission, a percentage of the client's payments. It is not uncommon for specialist manicurists to be self employed, buying the range of products from a supplier who guarantees a specific exclusive geographic area for trading.

Figure 1.7 Manicure can become a specialised career

Retail sales

Retail sales of beauty therapy-related products and personal equipment are made in a number of beauty salons, department stores and chemist/cosmetic chains. Sales are also generated through party plan and home visiting teams. Often working for a particular cosmetics manufacturer, the retail sales person will advise customers of the features and benefits of particular ranges of products and their suitability for use. Product ranges will include make-up, nail enamel, beauty treatment preparations, perfumes and beauty appliances. The retail sales person's salary is often supplemented by commission upon the sales made and performance will often be gauged by the level of sales undertaken by the sales person or their team. In some cases the sales person's income will be based entirely upon commission from sales.

When selling a particular range of make up, the sales person is usually expected to be able to demonstrate its application to the potential purchaser. Good communication and sales skills are required, as well as skills in make-up application (if relevant).

Sales technician

The correct and safe use of products and equipment is essential. Manufacturers and distributors of these often have, as part of their promotion team, a person who has the specialist skills to train people through demonstration.

Salons taking on new specialist equipment will usually be provided with, as part of the sales package, training for the staff in its correct use. This helps to ensure client satisfaction through correct and safe use. Legislation requires that the salon provides adequate training in the safe use of equipment.

When new products are introduced they will often be promoted through demonstration to the public at retail outlets, therefore building client demand, as well as being demonstrated to the professional either in the salon or at beauty-related exhibitions and trade events.

The demonstrator must have good presentation and communication skills, as well as sufficient specialist technical skills for the range being promoted. This job will often involve travel, with some time spent away from home. Often the technician will travel and work on their own in salons or shops with which she is unfamiliar. They will meet a wide number of professionals and members of the public and will have a high profile during these events.

Salary is often determined by the level of activity and sometimes sales. While the role is not directly one of selling, the underlying feature is one of supporting and encouraging sales.

Qualifications in the skills being demonstrated are required, particularly when providing this service to other company's salons.

Teacher/Instructor

Teaching and training people in a vocational setting can be very rewarding, providing the opportunity to contribute to the industry's future and to impart skills that you have acquired to others. This may take place in colleges of further education, private training schools or manufacturer's training centres. The teacher/instructor may work with people in a wide range of ages and at a variety of professional competence.

A high level of competence is required in the skills that are being taught. This will have been achieved through training and education, the achievement of qualification and professional commercial experience. The ability to offer a wide range of beauty therapy skills can be an advantage when seeking employment in this area. Good communication skills are required as well as having achieved or be working towards relevant teaching and/or training qualifications.

Salary may be determined by personal level of skill and duration of service in the beauty therapy industry. Salary would normally be a consistent basic salary and is not usually performance related.

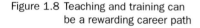

Figure 1.8 Teaching and training can be a rewarding career path

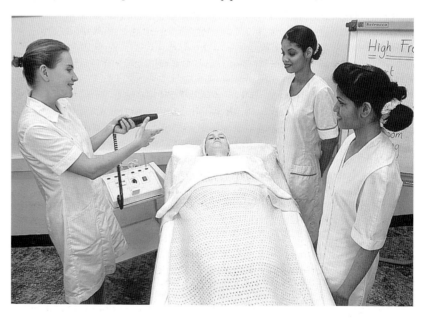

This list of roles in beauty therapy is not exhaustive but will provide you with an appreciation of the vast range of career opportunities available.

Continuing Professional Development

As a skilled professional your development will be ongoing. The beauty industry is continually developing new technologies and those working within these fields need to be conversant and competent in these areas.

Manufacturing companies often provide training and support for those working with their equipment and products. There are also a complete range of education and training programmes available from colleges of further education, private training centres and commercial academies. You may wish to consider developing your skills and knowledge while at the same time gaining further professional qualifications. The National Vocational Qualification framework currently offers a wide range of professional qualifications. Having achieved your level 3 award you may wish to develop skills in management and when in a management role work to the achievement of a Management award at NVQ/SVQ level 3,4 or 5. The exact level depending upon your particular management role. There are a range of awarding bodies which have professional qualifications for the beauty therapy industry, these include: City & Guilds of London Institute (C&G), Edexcel (BTEC), International Therapy Examination Council Limited (ITEC) and International Health & Beauty Council (IHBC). These awarding bodies have qualification structures which include broad band professional qualifications as well as very specific skills modules. Some are modular and have options which may be taken, others require you to follow a defined programme of learning. For some qualifications the prior achievement of additional qualifications may be an entry requirement.

PERSONAL CAREER ACTION PLAN

To support the achievement of your career goals a plan can help you to focus upon the actions required. For successful career progression you should have a planned route (a personal career action plan). Consider what you wish to achieve in your career, and when determining this think about your strengths and weaknesses. Chart how you might achieve these expectations, being realistic in considering a time scale for achievement.

As you progress in your career, review your career action plan. Be prepared to amend the plan in the light of your experience. It may turn out that you achieve milestones in your plan sooner than expected; this will require a change in part of the plan. The reverse may also apply. Through the experience of work you may wish to amend these. The career action plan is a dynamic document, always prepared to respond to change. In the light of changed expectations the route to achieve this will need to be mapped out. The entire process may be done either formally, as part of a work review and appraisal process, or informally, as a personal thought process. Without a personal career action plan, achievement will occur more by accident than by design, and time and experience may be wasted.

As part of your career development consider the following:

I objectively review your performance

I identify your strengths and weaknesses, awareness of these can help you to capitalise on the former and address the later

I make the most of opportunities to learn and develop skills

I always be prepared to watch specialists work (subject to available time and privacy)

l participate in any available relevant training activities

l be prepared to seek advice on issues relating to your job or your learning

l be prepared to participate fully in salon activities that will give you experience through which learning will take place.

As part of your employment you may be involved in the process of appraisal and review. This is an opportunity to review your performance since the previous appraisal and to plan future work with your line manager, personnel officer or training manager.

This process may focus on evaluating/responding to your training and development requirements. It becomes your opportunity to review your performance and to highlight those achievements that you consider noteworthy; advice may be given on areas of potential improvement (this should centre around your job description), and to negotiate and agree further training.

The personal skill check on pages 221–228 will help you determine your current stage of competence. You may use this to review your development towards your goal of achieving a beauty therapy award. Do this on a regular basis and set yourself realistic goals of achievement which may be reviewed at each review date.

Personal Career Action Plan

Name ....

Career goals (i.e. the type of job, the company I wish to work for):

....

....

The vocational experience I need to achieve this goal (types of work, length of service, skills to be developed):

experience ....

experience ....

experience ....

The academic qualifications I need to achieve this goal:

qualification ....

qualification ....

qualification ....

The vocational qualifications I need to achieve this goal:

qualification ....

qualification ....

qualification ....

Relevant experience to date:

experience ....

experience ....

experience ....

Relevant qualifications gained to date:

qualification ....

qualification ....

qualification ....

Action plan to achieve my goal.

This will include: training I require, qualifications I must achieve, experience I must acquire in order to achieve my career goal. Goals should be realistic and attainable.

training/ qualification/ experience	priority	planned start date	planned completion date	how I will action this
....	....	....	....	....
....	....	....	....	....
....	....	....	....	....

When I will review my personal action plan and goal.

....

2 Client care and consultation

Effective communication is an essential prerequisite for quality service to your client. To satisfy their need you must first establish what that need is and then advise upon the suitability and potential effectiveness of the service. This chapter will provide you with guidance in techniques of communication and the process of assessing your client's needs.

Level 3

Elements

11.1 Provide Consultation

11.2 Advise on and promote services and products to clients

11.3 Gain feedback from clients to improve services

CONTENTS

Introduction	27
Responding to your client	27
Pre-treatment assessment	29
Feedback	31
Summary	32
Further study	33
Review questions	33

INTRODUCTION

Your client must feel that you have a real concern about them and the service provided to them. Clients have the ultimate decision-making power as to where they obtain the service that they perceive they need. Therefore not only must the level of customer service be maintained at a high level, but also they must feel that the guidance being offered is based upon sound research and that good professional advice arises from the findings of this research.

Customer service focuses not only on making the client feel welcome, though this is important in itself, but also on identifying your clients' needs, responding to their reasonable requests, providing guidance, problem solving and gaining feedback upon their perception of the quality of this service.

While your client will have a good insight into their needs, their judgements will often be based upon how they feel, their limited knowledge of the range of treatments and services available, and advertising. Your role, as the professional therapist, is to determine your client's wishes and to undertake your own assessment of your client to gauge the suitability of the treatment, and to be able to provide advice, guidance and draw conclusions about the provision of the treatment.

RESPONDING TO YOUR CLIENT

Effective communication

Do not assume that there will be effective communication with your client and be aware that some clients may have sensory limitations. They may be hearing or sight disadvantaged and although such disadvantages may not be immediately apparent, they can be a barrier to effective communication. Some clients may inform you on their arrival that they have a special communication requirement; others may not consider this relevant or may actively strive to hide this. You, as the therapist, need to ensure effective communication in a sensitive manner. Language may also form a barrier to effective communication. Your client may have English as a second language and therefore may think and respond in a different language. This can slow down communication. Other clients may not understand the English language so care must be taken that communication and understanding does occur between yourself and your client. Dialect from different parts of the country can also create communication barriers, as can the use of highly technical jargon. When identifying potential contra-indications to treatment, care must be taken to ensure that your client understands what is being asked of them.

Information about services and products

Information about services and products should be provided only by those members of staff who are fully aware of their features and benefits. The receptionist must have a knowledge of the range of treatments available and the products being retailed for homecare use.

Requests about the duration of a treatment or an overview of what a treatment includes can be very helpful to a prospective client. Clients who have not visited your salon or undertaken beauty treatments will be more assured if they are aware of what to expect.

When a client requests information about the suitability of a particular treatment or product for themselves they should be invited to visit the salon. It can be unwise to provide this type of advice to a client of whom you have no knowledge. Advice or making recommendations about the suitability of treatments or products for an individual should only be given when you are able to assess the particular client and their needs. Skin types, etc. can only be effectively assessed if you have had 'face to face' contact with the client. Your advice and guidance will be then based upon your client assessment and your professional knowledge of a treatment or product. Remember, you are the expert in your field, your client may not always make the correct assessment of themselves.

At the reception

Respond to your client's arrival promptly; they should have priority over non-client-based activities. If you are undertaking company business, for example stock control or meeting with a sales representative, acknowledge your client's arrival.

This acknowledgement may be achieved by simply making eye contact with the client and smiling. If you are able welcome them verbally, then do so. You should either stop what you are doing, always leaving work areas in a safe condition, or excuse yourself from the sales representative and approach the client. If a colleague is close at hand politely ask them to serve the client.

When undertaking reception duty it is good practice to avoid treating this area as a staff meeting area, so that unless busy with a client you are able to attend to newly arrived clients promptly. Further guidance on this is provided in chapter 3.

Retail sales

If your client indicates that they have visited the salon to make a purchase of retail products, greet the client and, having determined their objective, offer to advise on the product range and its suitability. Some clients will show that they wish time to view the goods while others will request direction to the appropriate product to meet their requirements. For those clients who wish time to view the retail display, direct them towards this. You should remain available to provide advice and once the client indicates their need for assistance, usually by making eye contact with you, then move closer and offer advice (see chapter 3). Watch for signs of anxiety or confusion and if this is apparent, provide advice and guidance. For those clients who know what product is needed or show that they need guidance, this level of service should be provided.

While working with your client

Always acknowledge the presence of your client, even if you are busy attending to another. This may be done by making eye contact and, if it is appropriate, verbally. Do not talk to a client about their treatment while working with another; this is impolite and rather unprofessional. The client with whom you are working is entitled to have all your attention during this service, and failure to do this may create an unsafe situation. Talking to others while working with your client can also destroy the relaxed atmosphere that is often sought while providing treatments. Remember to respect the confidentiality of your client and therefore do

Figure 2.1 It is important to respond promptly to your client's arrival

TIP: For security reasons, avoid leaving your client alone and unobserved while handling retail products.

TIP: If there is any uncertainty about the suitability of a treatment for use on a particular client, seek advice from your supervisor or, if relevant, the manufacturer (many of which have dedicated professional helplines).

not encourage clients to remain in a cubicle when providing a treatment or discussing treatment with another.

While working with your client be observant and responsive to their needs. In the early stages of the treatment you should identify whether your client wishes to talk during the treatment or would rather remain silent, other than responding to questions relevant to the treatment.

Throughout the client's visit to the salon be observant of their body language, whether during the provision of a treatment or making a sale. Look for signs of discomfort, for example fidgeting, as this may indicate physical discomfort with a treatment being provided or emotional discomfort being caused through concerns about treatment time or suitability of product being sold. If you should identify a situation where the client is at risk, this should be dealt with immediately. If this is outside your sphere of responsibility, then immediately refer this to your supervisor. Take care when responding to this type of situation that you do not leave others at risk while dealing with it. When questioning your client about a previous treatment or contra-indication, unwillingness to make eye contact may indicate that the client has difficulty in talking about those subjects. This may be due to emotion or they may not wish to provide the response.

> **TIP:** Ensure that you are aware of your salon's confidentiality procedures so that you can correctly advise your client.

> **TIP:** Even if very busy, always take care to respond to your client in a professional and courteous manner.

PRE-TREATMENT ASSESSMENT

A comprehensive awareness of the treatment being offered is necessary for effective pre-treatment assessment. Pre-treatment assessment can often be quite searching and your client should be pre-briefed about this and its purpose. Your client should appreciate that this information will help you to determine the appropriate treatment for their needs. Your client may need to be assured that the information provided as part of the assessment process is of a confidential nature. You should not discuss the findings of a consultation with any other clients and only those responsible in the business.

Throughout your service you must maintain a professional and hygienic appearance (see chapter 4). During pre-treatment assessment you will need your client to develop trust in your professional ability, and your appearance can be an early part of the process in developing this trust. During assessment you will be searching, this should be undertaken in a sensitive, respectful and supportive manner. Your client may feel vulnerable at this time but your professional manner can reassure them. For the assessment to be complete it is essential that your client is able to provide information without feeling threatened.

The pre-treatment consultation is a service usually provided free of charge to the client as part of the treatment. Some salons do make a charge for the service, which is then deducted from the treatment cost when the client undertakes the treatment plan.

Questioning

Questioning of a personal nature should be undertaken in the cubicle, away from others. You should use sensitive questions which are relevant to the information required. If a question is asked that is not understood by your client, it should be rephrased to aid comprehension. Jargon or technical terms are best avoided if they are not an essential aspect of the questioning, as this can become a barrier to effective communication. Open-ended questions, those which require a response of more than yes

> **TIP:** Remember that your client should have a pleasant experience as a result of their visit. Effective communication can help to ensure that their wishes are addressed and that your client can feel relaxed.

Figure 2.2 Record your client's
responses carefully

TIP: Refer your client to their
General Practitioner if there are
suspected contra-indications.
Referals should be made without
causing undue alarm and
concern.

or no, should be used. If insufficient response is made, ask further questions. You must use your knowledge of the treatments provided and body language to decide whether additional questioning is required, either to determine appropriate treatment or to check the validity of the response provided by your client. Do not be judgemental about the responses provided to your questions. The relevant responses should be noted so that you can provide guidance and advice at the conclusion of this process. When questioning you may be seeking information about: reasons for requesting treatment, lifestyle, physical and emotional condition, previous treatments, medical conditions/history, contra-indications and homecare treatments.

Responses to questions should be noted as these may form part of your treatment plan. Noted responses will provide reference in the future should there be questions relating to your guidance and advice. These responses may be kept on your client's treatment record. Some beauty therapy salons have a pre-treatment questionnaire. This can provide prompts for appropriate questions to ask as well as a form to record responses. These completed forms must be treated as confidential and stored appropriately.

It must be confirmed with your client that you depend on full and frank responses to your questioning to enable you to provide good advice and guidance.

Physical examination

Dependant upon the nature of the treatment and the area of the body to be treated this stage of the pre-treatment, assessment can be stressful for your client. Advice upon pre-treatment assessment, suitability and purpose of particular treatments as well as contra-indications is provided in each chapter relating to treatments.

Physical examination should be carried out in the cubicle or gym area (for aspects of figure diagnosis). The area should be warm and comfortable for your client. If necessary, allow you client to change from their outdoor clothing into suitable clothing – this may be a towelling wrap or an exercise suit (for figure diagnosis). The client's clothing should be stored securely, usually in a locker, if a shared changing area is used. Personal privacy should be maintained, particularly when dealing with members of the opposite sex.

When examining unclothed areas of the body, the remainder of the body should be covered either with the robe or towelling. Cover the part of the body which has just been examined before moving to and exposing another. This will help to maintain personal dignity as well as body temperature.

You should always maintain high levels of hygiene when undertaking a physical examination (see chapter 4). Cleanse your hands both before and after the examination.

Using your treatment record card, record the date of the examination, the areas examined and the results. Remember it is as important to record findings which indicate non-contra-indications as well as contra-indications. In some cases the records will show your assessment of category, for example skin type, in others it may be fact, for example measurements. Physical examination may lead to additional questioning for clarification. The records of the examination are confidential and should be stored securely.

If your client experiences physical pain, the examination should end and your client be referred to their GP. Always be aware of your client's comfort. You should consider their body temperature as well as watching body language, which may indicate stress. Your responses to findings should confirm detail rather than be judgemental.

Evaluation

When the beauty therapist has gathered all the information then conclusions may be drawn and advice provided. It may be appropriate to give this advice immediately following the questioning and examination. However, if additional specialist information or advice is required, feedback should not be provided until all deliberations have taken place. Should specialist advice be needed, the client will usually appreciate that particular care is being taken in the consultation. This need not imply a lack of knowledge in the beauty therapist but the awareness of the therapist for the need for specialist advice.

Figure 2.3 Using computerised customer records

The findings of the consultation may lead to an obvious treatment or treatments requirement. In other cases there be a number of potential treatments and this may need you, the therapist, to prioritise. Such prioritisation may take the form of points scoring, where certain requirements are given a weighting according to their importance. The more important requirements score more highly and when the final analysis is made these will have a greater influence in the decision making than the less important features, even though these may outnumber the more important requirements. When there are options available these may require discussion with your client to determine their priority.

All conclusions and advice should be recorded on the client's treatment record. Should permissions be required from persons such as the client's GP, this should be obtained in writing and be attached to the record.

A written treatment plan should be produced: one copy for your client and one for the salon records and your reference. The treatment plan will be determined as a result of the questioning, physical examination and any subsequent research. It should indicate the nature of the treatment to be provided, the number of visits for the programme, their frequency, homecare treatments, the cost and payment plan (if available) and measurable outcomes.

You should explain the plan to your client and be prepared to respond to their questions, which may be about the benefits of the treatment, commitment to homecare treatment, costs and alternatives. It may be helpful to use any available visual aids, for example wall charts, to assist in explaining the treatment to your client. For your client to commit themselves to the programme they will need to understand all its implications and to agree that it is what they require. You should not make unrealistic and unattainable claims about the results which will be achieved.

Figure 2.4 Therapist using a chart to explain treatment

The treatment plan will require updating following each treatment and may need amendment as a result. Always consult and inform your client before changing the treatment plan.

Feedback

Throughout your service to the client obtain feedback by gathering information from your client about how they are perceiving the service. This feedback can provide you with guidance in the perceived quality of the service and how it is meeting the clients' expectations. You will be able to use this information to adjust the service delivery to better meet your clients' wishes.

Positive feedback – confirming service is meeting expectation – will inform you that you have provided the service in a manner which meets your clients' expectations.

Negative feedback – confirming service is not meeting expectation – should be viewed positively as a support to you adjusting or amending the service delivery to better meet your clients' expectations. Feedback may be obtained throughout the service delivery, following the service delivery and on a random basis.

As well as obtaining feedback regarding your own service delivery your salon may have a policy and procedure for obtaining feedback that is centrally monitored and used to guide your salon as a whole to improve service delivery and to ensure a quality provision.

Informal questioning may be used to obtain feedback. To provide a volume of feedback which can be used to evaluate the service provision of a questionnaire may be used. This will ensure that a range of persons are all asked to respond in the same manner and therefore provide quality data for review. When creating a questionnaire consider first what you want to find out. Design questions which will search those areas and that are easy and quick to respond to. This usually points towards the ranges of response choices being provided from which the client selects that which is most applicable. More information about the design and use of questionnaires is included in chapter 3.

Having collected data this feedback should be use to inform the salon and these findings should be passed to those who are responsible for the specific area. The feedback may confirm existing good practice on which to build. It may also provide indication of areas requiring corrective action. Once the corrective action has been taken this should be monitored via client feedback to ensure that their perceptions of change reflect your own.

All areas of service provision may be evaluated from client feedback, including:

l quality of service

l cost of service/value for money

l speed of service

l quality of salon environment

l range of service available.

A culture of using feedback in a positive manner to improve the quality of service provision is good business practice. Individual members of the team should be encouraged to obtain feedback to check on client comfort and satisfaction and to receive and use negative feedback positively. Feedback received should be passed on to the responsible person as soon as is practicable.

Salon managers may decide to provide feedback to the staff team regarding the feedback obtained from charts including celebrating positive attributes.

SUMMARY

You will have determined from this chapter that effective communication is the prominent feature in providing consultation. Communication can never be taken for granted and must always be checked out. Advice provided to your client will be based upon your knowledge of the treatment/product and your professional judgement of its suitability. The personal nature of the beauty therapy industry is such that this service must be provided with consideration for the client's personal feelings balanced with the requirement to supply good advice based upon the information available.

At the completion of the treatment programme it is good practice to evaluate its success. Has it achieved what you set out to achieve? If not, is there a valid reason? It is always very important not to make guarantees about products and treatments that may not be achievable; always be realistic. Always consult your client about their level of satisfaction of the treatment service and its achievements.

FURTHER STUDY

1. Observe your client's body language to extend your awareness of signs and their implications.
2. Design a questionnaire for use with your client prior to and during assessment.
3. Design a treatment plan form which will provide all information likely to be required by the client and the therapist.
4. Design a customer feedback form, for completion by your client at the end of the treatment programme.

Review questions

1. How should you respond to a client's arrival while treating another?
2. How should you respond to a client's arrival while negotiating with a sales representative?
3. Suggest one feature of body language that indicates discomfort?
4. What is open-ended questioning?
5. What features should be included in the treatment plan?
6. Describe positive feedback.
7. Suggest 3 areas which may be monitored through a client questionnaire.

3 Effective working practices

This chapter will provide you with an overview of those features of good working practice both as a beauty therapist and as a person responsible for others at work. You will find references to other chapters in this book which will provide additional information.

Level 3

Elements

11.1 Provide individual consultation services

11.2 Advise on and provide services and products to clients

11.3 Gain feedback from clients to improve services

12.1 Contribute to the effective use of resources

12.2 Contribute to effective productivity within the salon

13.1 Maintain safe working practices within the salon

CONTENTS

Introduction   35

Projecting the image   35

Efficient working practices   35

Maintaining services and operations   38

Sales   41

Making the Sale   42

Consumer legislation (Law)   44

Summary   45

Further study   45

Review questions   46

INTRODUCTION

The effective operation of the beauty therapy salon is the result of a team of people. All of those working in the salon have a responsibility for the success of the business. Such success is achieved through the quality of the service they provide to the clients and to each other. This includes those who work in a support role as well as those who work in direct contact with clients.

Your client is the decision maker who determines where they spend their beauty therapy budget. Their perception of the business is based upon the accumulation of data absorbed during their visit and therefore the results of all of those who work in the business.

The management of this operation has the responsibility for maintaining the quality of the service and operation.

PROJECTING THE IMAGE

The outward appearance of you as a beauty therapist will project an image and message to your client and those with whom you work. It will create expectations of the quality and style of service that can be expected. For the new client those first impressions can be so important as this is when they form their lasting impression. The therapist who attends the client appearing in a clean overall or uniform will be creating an efficient and professional image. The client can have confidence that if this aspect is attended to then all other aspects both in front and behind the scenes will be of a similar standard. The therapist can inform the client of the style of their treatment and the belief that they hold in them by their appearance. The hairstyle, the make-up and style of shoes worn can convey messages to the client. A totally neutral appearance, with hair held back off the face and minimum make-up will project an image which will be not only hygienic but also non-offensive to a range of clients (see chapter 4 for more details). Media and legislation has set levels of expectation that the client may hold and will expect. Everyone is an individual and will have a differing physical appearance, however, the beauty therapist is an emissary for the beauty therapy industry and the services it provides, and therefore should have a regard for their appearance and use the service to maximise their image.

As a manager or supervisor it is your responsibility to act as a role model for those you work with, setting an example of good practice in both appearance and working practices. Your appearance can inform your staff of the image that you expect to be maintained and you can demonstrate through your actions how this image may be maintained throughout the working day. It can be unrealistic for those for whom you are responsible to aspire to standards for that you do not practise.

EFFICIENT WORKING PRACTICES

Communication

Effective communication is essential to ensure that the requirements of others are determined and that they understand yours. This will be focused on throughout this book as it is such an important part of providing a service.

Figure 3.1 Effective communication is essential

Your client will generally be more comfortable if they are aware of the treatment procedure to which they are about to commit. Information can be given when they are booking and paying for a programme of treatments or when they are about to undertake the treatment itself. For your client to be able to relax, which often has a positive effect on the treatment outcome, they need to be assured of what is about to happen and for this information to be provided in a professional and knowledgeable manner. Be prepared to respond to questioning about the treatment and comparisons with other treatments, etc. Remember that your client's questioning will enable you to reassure and engender confidence in your professional ability. This need to communicate is even more important when the treatment is provided to your client for the first time. The client may need to know how long the treatment will take, as they may have other commitments and could become restless if they are uncertain whether they will be able to meet these. They need to be aware of what the treatment entails so avoid technical jargon that they may not understand. Avoid detail which can be off putting but, at the same time, be honest. Be attentive to your client's emotions and feelings; you must develop the ability to determine the correct level and style of explanation which is applicable to each client. By providing information about the treatment, your client can sometimes be made more aware of conditions that may contra-indicate this, which they may not previously have considered relevant.

Information given to your client should be concise and appropriate. Avoid confusing the explanation with unnecessary additions or technical terms that your client may not understand. If you are unable to provide all the information required or a knowledgeable response to a question, it is generally better to be honest and admit this and undertake to obtain this information. It can be unrealistic to hold all the information required without forewarning. It is essential that all information and advice is accurate and not misleading (Trades Description Act later in this chapter). Any guidance about treatments should be noted on your client's treatment plan, which may then be referenced later.

Efficiency

Treatment times

Efficient working practices are required not only to ensure that a service is provided to your client but also that it is provided in a professional, cost effective and hygienic manner.

In the beauty therapy industry most services are supplied to your client on a one to one basis, therefore the service has considerable customer focus. Your client must feel that they are the centre of your attention and that the service revolves around their needs (see chapter 5). In providing the client-focused approach you must not lose sight of the other aspects of efficiency.

When the prices of your services were determined one of the major considerations will have been the time that the therapist spends with the client in providing this. Supplying the treatment in the recognised time allowance is important if the business is to function efficiently and profitably.

The time allowance for each treatment should be sufficient to allow the treatment to be provided effectively. Over running these times can cause a delay for clients arriving later. These delays can be distressing for the client and stressful for the therapist. This can result in treatments being provided

TIP: When first joining the staff team of a beauty salon find out the length of time allocated to each treatment.

in an atmosphere which is not conducive to their full benefits. If you do over run, due to an unforeseen circumstance, it may be necessary to negotiate with colleagues to assist and possibly undertake some treatment provision. If you are unsure of the acceptability of this practice then you should discuss it with your supervisor or line manager.

Prolonging treatment due to inefficient working practice can, in certain treatments, cause client discomfort. If the body has been pre-warmed for a treatment the beneficial effects can be lost if the treatment is prolonged. Your client may experience discomfort if they have to remain in a position for a lengthy period or if a treatment is extended in a particular area for too long.

Product usage

Wastage of material and unnecessary breakage of equipment will reduce business efficiency. Treatments are normally costed with a specified level of product usage, not only consumable products but also those which are reusable; for example, towels and blankets. The use of individually packaged products can be an efficient method of controlling product use. These products are generally more expensive than those that are provided in bulk, however, this can be countered by the savings made. In some cases the use of individually packaged products can fulfil a client expectation of the apparent quality of the product being used as well as reassurance that the product is in good condition. When a product is packaged individually for hygienic purposes, for example the electrolysis needle, this feature should be demonstrated to the client and care must be exercised to ensure that a level of hygiene is maintained once the package is opened. When a product is provided in bulk you should take care that you only use the appropriate amount. In some cases there are dispensers and applicators to provide a measured quantity, which can help to maintain efficient product use. If no such dispensing provision is made, you must take care when removing product to avoid spillage and wastage. Use a measured quantity, which may be varied according to need.

Once any product has been removed from a bulk container it should not be returned. When the product is removed it will become contaminated. This contamination can come from dust particles in the atmosphere, unclean utensils or contamination from the therapist or client. Should any contaminated product be returned to a bulk container it may contaminate the rest of the product. This could cause cross infection from client to client or act as a catalyst and bring about a reaction in the product leading to deterioration. When removing the product from tubs and jars a sterile spatula should be used to prevent contamination of the jar's contents. Replace lids as soon as possible to avoid contamination and accidental spillage. Keep bulk containers clean and in prime condition. Do not allow a build up of the product around the neck or opening of containers as this can cause contamination and give a very unhygienic appearance. If your client is to see these containers they should be maintained so that they show the product is in good condition. Avoid faded or stained labels and products which have separated as the client may be concerned that the product is aged and no longer at its best.

If you decant bulk products into smaller containers, do not use containers that may be confused or mistaken for other products. This can be misleading to your client as well as increasing the risk of accidental misuse by the therapist.

Do not allow products to be used on more than one client as this can encourage cross infection; for example, lip stick or eye shadow. These

TIP: Providing an efficient service means planning ahead; have all the required equipment and materials prepared beforehand.

TIP: Your client will gain considerable reassurance if your levels of hygienic actions are apparent.

TIP: It is bad practice to decant products into containers that are then not labelled or retain a label from previous use.

TIP: Products which have been contaminated should be disposed of hygienically, usually in a sealed plastic sack. Do not dispose of toxic waste in the sink.

substances should first be scraped onto a spatula, into a dish or onto a palette for individual use with your client.

Take care not to leave products in places where they become a hazard to you, your client or your colleagues. Always ensure that products are replaced in their appropriate storage place as soon as possible following their use. Failure to promptly return these products to their normal storage location can also cause delays for colleagues who require them for their clients.

The use of disposable covers, such as tissue roll, can reduce the wear and tear on blankets, etc. These items do have a cost factor and should therefore be used sparingly.

Equipment usage

Never use equipment with which you are not familiar. If you are in any doubt you should seek guidance from your supervisor or line manager. It is good practice to retain manufacturer's guidance notes for correct use either with the equipment or in a salon-based file.

Before use always check equipment for outward signs of damage or wear and tear. It is unwise and can be dangerous to use equipment which shows any sign of damage, and injury caused through using equipment that is knowingly damaged or unsafe can result in litigation. All businesses should have a procedure for reporting hazards that should be complied with. It is good practice to report such hazards as soon as reasonably possible following its identification rather than waiting until the equipment is next required for use.

Figure 3.2 Accurate client records are needed to help a salon function efficiently

MAINTAINING SERVICES AND OPERATIONS

To maintain efficient service and operation the business performance must be monitored, not only in its financial aspects but also in its function. The efficient operation of the business function will have a direct effect upon the financial efficiency of the business.

Customer feedback

Feedback from your customers can be used to determine their level of satisfaction and to identify areas of potential improvement. Feedback can be obtained by actively asking your clients their views and recording their responses; this is generally most effectively done by a questionnaire. Questionnaires may be used with all clients all the time, with a random number of clients all the time, or with all clients for set periods of time. To gain your client's co-operation the questionnaires should be designed for quick and accurate completion.

When designing your questionnaire about your client's perception of the service, first decide what you wish to find out and then design questions or statements that will obtain this information. Ensure that your questions can be understood by your client and that they cover topics on which the client will be able to form an opinion. To enable these responses to be analysed it is often more effective to provide the client with a number of options to respond to, with the opportunity to add comments if considered relevant. The options provided may be as points to be allocated, for example 1 to 10 where 1 = poor and 10 = excellent, or the options may be provided with statements which are selected as appropriate, for example poor, average, very good. A pre-determined range of responses can facilitate speedy analysis of the number of people making certain responses, which can then provide guidance about your client's perceptions. It can be useful to obtain some information about your clients at the same time; for example, their age or gender. This can assist in segmenting the types of responses to determine if there are patterns of perception which relate to certain types of client. Before using any questionnaire it should be tested on a small number of people to check if it is understandable and produces the information which you require. Once this has been confirmed it is then ready for use. Alternative methods of obtaining feedback can be used; for example, client interviews where your client is asked to respond to a number of questions, or focus groups, where small groups of clients meet to discuss the quality of the service provided and give feedback.

The results of the survey should be used to provide you with a view of your client. This may not dictate the way that the service is supplied but it can assist as one tool to be used in determining the service. It can also provide a guide that may uncover problems of which you were not previously aware and that once made apparent may be dealt with.

Complaints about services or treatments

Clients who return to the salon with a complaint about a service or treatment should be treated politely. Avoid appearing irritable and respond calmly and with empathy but without acknowledging any responsibility. Once you have established that the client has a complaint, ask them to take a seat in the customer waiting area and promptly refer to the person in the business who is responsible for dealing with complaints. In the first place this may be the therapist, subsequently this may be the manageress or proprietor. Complaints about service or treatment should be discussed in private, either in an office or an area away from other clients.

The exact nature of the complaint should be established by talking to the client. Do this in a seated position as it helps to diffuse the situation. Establish the facts and check these out: dates of appointment, actual treatment records, charges. Undertake all of this in a calm, non-judgemental manner. Remember that having dealt with the problem it is in the salon's best interest, in most cases, for the client to continue to visit for treatments.

Many salons will have Professional Indemnity Insurance to provide compensation in cases when it can be shown that the salon has been at fault. Remember that all insurance companies who provide this type of policy will have procedures with which to comply. You should never admit liability without guidance from your insurance company.

Once the nature of the complaint has been determined, the person responsible must decide what action to take. When a complaint is unfounded an explanation of the problem can often be sufficient, separating and dealing with each aspect of the complaint step by step. It is important for the client to accept the outcome as this avoids subsequent actions by them. When a complaint is justified a judgement may be made to provide treatments to remedy the problem without accepting liability.

When the problem requires compensation or further action, it may be necessary to consult your insurance company for guidance in appropriate actions. In all cases detailed records should be kept about conversations, statements, claims and subsequent agreements made with clients.

ABINGDON COLLEGE
LEARNING CENTRE

Staff performance

Effective communication with your staff team is an important part of maintaining services and operations. Most staff need to feel part of the team where their opinion and input is valued. A very effective method of communicating business information is through regular staff meetings. These should be provided for all staff to participate in. For meetings to be effective the staff team should be given adequate notice to ensure their attendance. An agenda or list of topics should be produced either beforehand or at least at the beginning of the meeting. The meeting will require a person to lead or 'chair' and any agreements should be noted so that subsequent actions can be monitored. The leader should make certain that those who wish are allowed to participate and that those who are less forthcoming are encouraged and allowed to participate. If opinions are sought they should be considered and not disregarded if they do not fit with prior expectations. The leader will need to manage the meeting to ensure that it reaches its objectives in the time available and that contributions are gained from all concerned without become side tracked.

The staff meetings can be the ideal opportunity to: give information to the staff team about the business and its procedures; inform staff about changes; inform staff about forthcoming plans and events; supply feedback to the team as a whole; and allow staff to make comments and suggestions.

Another method of communication with the staff team is by a staff notice board. This gives the opportunity to confirm agreements from meetings or to post information and notices which are required to be displayed; for example, health and safety information. There is, however, no guarantee that staff will read this.

Review and appraisal of each member of staff's performance is a tool to be used to provide feedback and identify views, needs and targets of achievement. The appraisal system allows both the appraiser and appraisee to review previous performance as well as to look forward and negotiate future actions. Through appraisal you may confirm with your staff the description of their job role and the required standards of performance; it is the employees chance to confirm their perceptions of their job role and responsibilities. It will provide the opportunity to: identify any professional needs of the member of staff; identify any training and development needs; negotiating any targets which are set – targets of performance, target dates; and identify support required by the member of staff to enable the necessary quality of service to be maintained. These agreements should be recorded and then viewed at the next appraisal to determine achievement on both sides.

Targets for levels of performance may be set at regular intervals. This often relates to levels of income from the clients, numbers of specific treatments, conversions of clients from one treatment to another or levels of retail sales. Targets are most effective when they are negotiated rather than imposed. They should be realistic and attainable; targets which cannot be met will lead to despair by the staff. Achieving a target can motivate and allow for further target setting. Achievement of targets is normally recognised by some kind of incentive, usually financial. In setting targets, health and safety must also be taken into account; do not set targets which push people to cut corners or to place others at risk.

Take care to respect the self esteem and confidentiality of your staff team. Providing feedback to individuals should be undertaken in confidence and not in front of colleagues or clients.

Figure 3.3 A staff meeting might be called to evaluate a new product

TIP: Negotiating performance targets that are SMART will provide clear indicators against which to review:

S – stated/specific

M – measurable

A – achievable/agreed

R – relevant

T – timebound.

A regular review of individual and team performance should be made. This should focus on the quality of the service, health and safety, and efficiency. Computerised management information systems, including the client billing system, can usually provide information about performance in a variety of ways, including number of clients, the average bill size, individual staff activity, activity in a particular treatment, etc. This can be an efficient tool for monitoring business effectiveness. When reviewing business effectives any external factors which may not be recorded must be born in mind; for example, extreme bad weather can have an effect on business.

Responsibilities

In the business there will be people who have responsibility for maintaining safe working conditions (see chapter 4). It is essential that the people who assume these responsibilities keep up to date with current requirements.

SALES

Your client may purchase beauty retail products for home use from a variety of outlets. These include large chemist chains, supermarkets, department stores, party plan home shopping, Internet and the beauty therapy salon. Some of these retail outlets are able to offer goods at very competitive prices, as they are able to purchase in very large volumes from manufacturers or distributors, therefore maximising discounts from bulk purchase. In some cases the outlet may have its own brand which it promotes, using the media of television and consumer magazines. In other cases the outlet is able to capitalise upon the convenience angle, with the customer being able to fulfil their cosmetics requirements while completing their family grocery shopping. Many beauty therapy salons do not have access to these benefits, but they do have certain unique features to offer.

In most cases the beauty therapy salon can offer products of quality and at the same time provide professional advice in the correct selection and use. The retail product range can link with the product being used during the salon-based treatment and therefore compliment and reinforce the benefits derived. This can often be highlighted in the treatment plan by the beauty therapist and is an ideal route to introduce the client to retail goods. Many brands are promoted in the consumer press by the manufacturer directing the consumer to their beauty therapy salon, and in some cases the product availability can be restricted exclusively to the professional beauty salon. To capitalise on these unique features your client must be made aware of their features and availability.

There are career opportunities for the therapist to be a consultant offering this advice and guidance on product selection and its application on behalf of the manufacturer, distributor or wholesaler. The therapist uses their beauty therapy skills and knowledge in conjunction with promotion skills.

Stock is a valuable commodity and should be regarded as business capital, that is, an investment which will produce a financial return. Therefore it is important that stock is maintained in good condition, fit for sale and only the minimum investment is made in order to recoup the financial return without unnecessarily 'tying up' capital that could be generating interest in a capital savings account.

Stock can deteriorate if not stored and rotated correctly. Stock rotation ensures that the stock which has been held for the longest period is either used or presented for sale before the newer stock. Stock which becomes outdated will not generate a financial return and will actually cause a loss of money to the business when it has to be disposed of. As with purchasing any goods it is important to ensure that the goods purchased for resale are received correctly and in good order and steps are taken to redress this if it is not the case.

MAKING THE SALE

To advise your client effectively on the correct selection of retail goods, it is important that you are aware of the product range, and the individual product's features and benefits. You should know what the product is designed to do, any unique characteristics of the product that make it different from others and its suitability for different clients. The unit sizes and prices should also be known. Spend time finding out about your products as well as the products supplied by competitors. This will assist you when explaining to your customer why they should purchase a particular product from yourself.

Buying signs

When visiting the salon your client may express an interest in purchasing retail products in a variety of ways. This may be a direct request for a product such as from a client who enters the salon wishing to view the range, or a client whose interest is generated while they are in the salon receiving treatment and who shows interest by asking questions of the therapist about homecare products. You must be prepared to identify and build on these signals of interest. Less obvious signals can include the client lingering by the retail stand, reading the labels on the products, handling the goods and looking in the mirror by the retail stand in an attempt to identify the suitable 'skin type' for the product.

Questions and suggestions

To find out your client's wishes, you may have to ask questions. Use open-ended questions which enable you to gain information; for example 'what is your skin type', 'which colour do your prefer', 'is the perfume for day wear or special occasions'. You must know what the client is looking for in order to advise them.

Find out what products your client currently uses. This can provide guidance to their normal spend level and quality of product. Do not be afraid to 'up sell'; that is, recommend a product from in a higher price range if it is appropriate. Be prepared to make suggestions and recommendations.

Never assume; always ask and confirm. If a client selects a product, check to determine if any other products are required. Should a selected product be part of a set or range, indicate the additional options to your client. If you have promotional offers which may suit the client's requirements, introduce these to your client.

When providing suggestions about the suitability of particular goods take care not to make extravagant claims about what the products can do. One of the features of the Trade Description Act 1968 is that it prohibits false claims being made about products (more information is provided later in this chapter).

TIP: Your unique selling feature is your professional knowledge; ensure that you are familiar with the products that you sell.

TIP: Do not be embarrassed by the price of your retail product lines. If the price is appropriate for the product it should not be a barrier to the sale. There is often a perceived value in a product from the price that is paid.

TIP: Always be prepared to 'up sell', if appropriate – to offer products of higher quality as an option, if available. Never assume that the client cannot afford or does not regard themselves highly enough to invest in themselves.

Always question your client about possible hypersensitivity, particularly when selling products which the manufacturer indicates can cause sensitivity.

Your client may ask for your view about the suitability of a particular retail product. In some cases you may have factual information or guidance that can direct, in other cases your comments may be based upon your own preferences. In these cases do not be judgemental, but provide your opinion and indicate that is your opinion and may differ from that of others. You may be volunteering opinion about what you perceive they may like as opposed to what you like. Allow your client to form their own final judgement based upon your opinion and their own view.

> **TIP:** Features of the product are what it does and how it does it. A product may have features that are unique and quite different from others. Benefits of the product are the advantages obtained, by the client, in their use.

Overcoming objections

Should your client demonstrate resistance to the sale, find out what the problem is by questioning. Break problems down into small parts and deal with each one at a time. Large problems can appear insurmountable, but when broken down into smaller parts and dealt with individually they can appear quite trivial and are more easily responded to in a positive manner.

Advise your client about the product and which of the range will suit their requirements. Be prepared to explain about the features and benefits more fully. Ultimately it is your client who will make the decision to purchase and it is your role to ensure that the products are presented and explained appropriately and their positive aspects highlighted.

Never be afraid of an objection as this can provide you with the opportunity to promote and confirm the feature and benefits of the product.

Figure 3.4 Therapist applying a sample of foundation

Testers and samples

The use of testers and samples can enable the client to try the product on themselves, with guidance from the therapist. It may be necessary for the therapist to demonstrate to the client how a particular home use product can be used to best effect or to confirm its suitability for a particular client type. Take care to maintain high levels of hygiene with regard to cross infection from testers. Always use clean spatulas or pads to extract the product from the sample stand. Keep the display looking fresh and tidy but also accessible to the client. When the client tries the product they are confirming their interest in it.

When demonstrating a range of products, for example fragrances, it may be necessary to make notes about each and to summarise to encourage an objective judgement. To avoid confusion when presenting a range of fragrances to your client, place a small sample on an absorbent strip and waft under their nose, having given time for the propellant to evaporate. Avoid contact with the skin as this will help to reduce the fragrance lingering and influencing the effect of later samples.

Some fragrances and their carriers can cause skin reactions; always explain to your client that should this occur the product use should be ended and if the irritation continues a referral to their GP is recommended. When there is a known hypersensitivity by your client then consider the use of differing styles of fragrance carriers, including cream fragrances or eau de toilette, as these can be gentler upon the skin.

> **TIP:** Free sample packs can help to generate client interest and awareness of retail product lines and can provide a talking point around which a sale may be generated.

Figure 3.5 Therapist demonstrating perfume

Figure 3.6 Closing the sale

Closing the sale

Encourage your client to handle the product; holding the product and reading the label is a strong indicator of the client accepting the sale. Check, by questioning, which products your client wishes to purchase. Inform them of any choices with regard to size of product and range available. Package the products and confirm with your client their total spend.

Selling: the four-step approach

- create the interest – attract your client to the product through display, talk about the products that you retail
- generate the need – show your client how they may benefit from the use of the product
- overcome objections – deal with resistance to the sale, competitors products and suitability of the product, etc.
- close the sale – confirm the purchase.

CONSUMER LEGISLATION (LAW)

Consumer Protection Act 1987

This Act makes provision in respect of liability for damage caused by defective products. Product liability provides for the producer of a product, any person putting their name to the product and any person importing a product to be potentially liable for any damage caused by that product.

The Act makes it an offence to give a misleading indication of the price of goods and/or services. Products used by or sold to clients if proven to have caused damage, whether faulty or not, may result in compensation being sought as well as possible criminal prosecution.

Sale of Goods Act 1979

This Act provides the consumer with the right to expect a product to be of 'merchantable quality', that is, fit for the purpose for which it was sold. It provides the consumer with the right to seek a refund or replacement for the product should it be shown not to be of appropriate quality or as described. The refund or replacement should be provided by the retailer, who may subsequently take a similar action with their supplier. Proof of purchase may be required and a credit note need not be accepted by the client, though it may be offered by the business.

This relates to the beauty therapy salon which retails products. Should the product not perform correctly, for example, an aerosol which does not function, the client may demand a replacement or refund. The issue is between the retailer and the customer.

Supply of Goods and Services Act 1982

This Act requires that a person providing a service must do so with reasonable care and skill; for example, a therapist providing a treatment must do so with a proper standard of workmanship. Unless otherwise agreed, the treatment should be provided in a reasonable time and for a reasonable charge. The term 'reasonable' is decide by comparing this with the normal standard for supplying that particular service. The later two areas apply only when nothing is previously stated about the time scale or price.

In beauty therapy, most treatments are priced and the time scale agreed before the commencement of the regime. It is reasonable to expect the treatment to be carried out with a degree of care and skill, and, if not, compensation may be sought if the case proven.

Trade Descriptions Act 1968

This Act prohibits any false descriptions of goods including:

I quantity and size

I method of manufacture

I composition

I fitness for the purpose, strength, performance and behaviour

I physical characteristics

I testing and/or approval by any person

I place, dates and person who manufactured

I any other history.

The Act prohibits false trade descriptions about services provided.

In a beauty therapy context this may affect claims about products and treatments, their effects, contents, production history, etc.

SUMMARY

You should now have an overview that centres on efficient working practice. As the beauty therapist you have the task of providing a customer-focused service within the constraints of business. Clients have a heightened awareness of customer service and while the service they receive is an important feature, it is their perception of the quality of the service that may make the difference and cause them to select you for treatment rather than another.

As a person with responsibility in the business you have the role of monitoring the quality, efficiency of the service provided and the environment in which this takes place. Views and opinions of all concerned must be actively sought and these views used as a tool to enable you to continually evaluate and improve the service.

FURTHER STUDY

1. To aid your effective working, create a file of manufacturer's guidelines for use of equipment and products which you may refer to or refer your colleagues to.

2. Create a customer feedback questionnaire and with permission from your supervisor use this with your clients to monitor your service.

3. Undertake a review of your performance, time the duration of the treatments that you undertake and compare these to the industry norms. This may help you identify personal development needs.

4. Review your own professional appearance, evaluate the image you project and if relevant plan how you may change this image.

Review questions

1. How should the product be hygienically extracted from a tub or jar?

2. What Act of Parliament requires the correct description of products and treatments effects?

3. How would you ensure hygienic use of an eye shadow from one client to another?

4. What is the purpose of appraisal?

5. What action should be taken if damage to equipment is identified?

6. Which Act of Parliament provides the consumer with the right to expect a product to be of merchantable quality?

7. How should confidential information, gained from your client, be treated?

8. Suggest one method by which you, as a supervisor, can provide guidance to your colleagues about salon procedures.

Working safely

This chapter will provide you with guidance in the safe working practices that are required in the beauty therapy industry, both by your clients and by legislation (law). Once you have read this chapter you should be able identify and understand the need to maintain quality in the service you provide to your clients and to focus on the need for safe and hygienic practices.

Elements

12.1 Contribute to the effective use of resources

13.1 Maintain safe working practices within the salon

13.2 Monitor and maintain salon security

18.2 Prepare the work area and client for the application of make up

CONTENTS

Introduction	48
Legislation	48
Maintaining a safe working environment	50
Your professional appearance	54
Instruments and equipment	56
Working with your clients	59
Monitoring	59
Salon security	61
Summary	63
Further study	63
Review questions	64

INTRODUCTION

Anybody at work has a legal obligation not to put themselves or others at risk, either by their actions or omissions. This places considerable responsibility upon you, the beauty therapist, as you will work not only with colleagues but also with your clients, the members of the public. There are a number of legislative regulations that specify these responsibilities: some are the responsibility of the salon owner (or person responsible) and some are the responsibility of the employee.

Your clients will have an awareness, heightened by the current increased focus on safety and hygiene, and may expect to see evidence of your hygiene procedures. Although you may well implement hygienic practices your client will require to see these being demonstrated.

You should set an example of good practice to others who work with you. Always strive to maintain an awareness of the quality of the service that you provide. Objectively review and evaluate this quality and set yourself and those for whom you have responsibility targets of service quality.

LEGISLATION

Hygiene

Businesses, where there may be a risk of cross infection, are often the subject of legislation that requires the registration of the business premises and for that business to maintain standards of hygiene. This applies to the beauty therapy salon.

The Local Government (Miscellaneous Provisions) Act 1982

This Act requires that any person carrying out ear piercing or electrolysis should be registered with their local authority and that these services should be conducted in registered premises. The Act enables local authorities to make bye-laws to set required standards of:

l cleanliness of premises and its fittings

l cleanliness of the registered persons and their assistants

l cleaning, and where appropriate, sterilising of equipment used by the registered person.

The Act gives powers for an authorised officer of the local authority to enter a business premise by way of a warrant granted by a justice of the peace. Breaches of the regulations can result in registration being removed and a fine may be imposed.

Bye-laws

Although these are laws which are made locally, they are, nevertheless, legal requirements and enforceable. The Local Government (Miscellaneous Provisions) Act empowers local authorities to require that all salons where either ear piercing or electrical epilation takes place register the premises and comply with a range of hygiene measures. These typically include:

l cleanliness and repair of all surfaces, furniture and fittings

l hygienic storage and disposal of waste products from the salon

l hygienic disposal of used needles – sharps box

l hygienic storage of needles for reuse (reuse of needles is now rarely done)

I daily disinfecting of couches and seats used by clients

I use of clean disposable paper over couches for each client

I non-smoking policy

I cleanliness of clients' protective covering

I sterile equipment used with ear piercing and electrolysis

I adequate sterilising facilities

I supply of clean hot and cold water

I storage space to eliminate, as far as is possible, the risk of cross contamination

I the operator must: have hands and nails washed clean and nails kept short
  – wear a clean and washable overall or disposable covering
  – cover any open wound, boil or sore which is exposed using an impermeable dressing
  – not smoke or consume food
  – wear a clean face mask and surgical gloves if known to be a Hepatitis B Surface Anagen Carrier

I the proprietor must provide adequate:
  – washing facilities
  – toilet facilities
  – first aid materials.

Non-compliance may result in a fine and removal of registration.

> **TIP:** Legislation may change and be updated so try to maintain your awareness of current legislation. Remember, ignorance of requirements is not always an acceptable excuse for non-compliance. Your local authority or the Office of Fair Trading may be able to provide you with current information.

Safety

Health and Safety at Work Act 1974 (HASAWA)

The employer has a duty of care to employees and others in the salon or those affected by the work of the salon. Employees have a duty not to intentionally endanger the health, safety and welfare of themselves or others. Employees must not interfere with or misuse any items provided in the pursuance of health and safety.

Control of Substances Hazardous to Health Regulations (COSHH)

This Regulation requires employers to consider potential hazards to people exposed to substances in the salon. This includes assessing substances for potential hazards, having identified any potential hazard to consider possible alternative less hazardous substances that may be used, and to set up safe working procedures. This Regulation also covers harmful fumes and gases which may be produced by using electrical equipment.

The Workplace (Health, Safety and Welfare) Regulations 1992

This Regulation applies to all workplaces and sets minimum standards of facilities and the provision of safe premises in which to work.

The Manual Handling Operations Regulations 1992

This Regulation requires that employers assess an individual's capability to carry or move stock and for guidance to be provided in safe working practices.

The Personal Protective Equipment at Work Act 1992

This Act requires employers to provide, free, suitable personal protective equipment to employees who may be exposed to risk at work. Employees must report to the employer any loss or damage of these provisions.

Figure 4.1 How to lift heavy cartons. Always lift bending the knees and keeping the back straight

The Electricity at Work Regulations 1989

This Regulation requires employers to maintain all electrical equipment and installations in a safe condition. Employees have a responsibility to report any faulty electrical equipment that they come across in the workplace.

The Provision and Use of Work Equipment Regulations 1992

This Regulation requires that an employer should provide equipment that is suitable for its use and properly maintained and that all staff are trained to use it safely.

First Aid Regulations 1981

Every employer must provide adequate and appropriate equipment and facilities for first aid.

Reporting of Injuries, Diseases and Dangerous Occurrences Regulations 1985 (RIDDOR)

This Regulation provides a listing of industrial diseases and disorders that must be reported to the Health and Safety Inspectorate. These include potentially infectious conditions. Accidents at work which require hospitalisation or long periods of absence from work must also be reported.

MAINTAINING A SAFE WORKING ENVIRONMENT

The current Health and Safety at Work Act requires that all those people at work comply with all reasonable requests by employers in the pursuance of the Act. Guidelines provided by your employer for safe working practices should be followed. If at any time you are uncertain of procedures, ask your line manager or person responsible for guidance about safety in your salon.

Safe working practices

All areas of the salon should be kept tidy, and walkways, stairs, entrances and exits should be kept clear. Avoid a build up of rubbish, particularly flammable papers and boxes, in the salon as these can become fire hazards. Waste products should be stored in covered bins which should be emptied at least once a day, but in hot weather more frequent emptying may be necessary to avoid unpleasant odours. Storing paper and boxes under staircases is bad practice as if there is a fire they may become fire centres.

Spillage of liquids and powders can cause extremely slippery floor conditions, so always clean up any spillages as soon as possible and warn others of the risk. Damaged or unsafe surfaces, fixtures and fittings should be reported to the person responsible. This is especially important if the hazard is likely to place yourself, your colleagues or your clients at risk. If you have a hazard reporting procedure in your salon, make sure you comply with it.

If you are uncertain or have not been instructed in the safe use of equipment or products, consult the manufacturer's guidelines or ask your supervisor for guidance.

Do make sure that you are aware of your salon's fire and evacuation procedures. Your salon will be licensed by the local authority who will in

**HEALTH AND SAFETY**:

Thoroughly cleanse your hands whenever you complete working with a client or move from one client to another. This will reduce the risk of cross infection passing from one client to another.

turn issue procedures. It is wiser to be fully aware of these before the need to use them arises. Procedures will require prompt action and indicate:

▌ who to inform, in the salon, of a fire

▌ how to recognise a fire or smoke alarm

▌ who will contact the emergency services and how this is done

▌ how the salon is to be evacuated, what the exit routes are and where and to whom you will all report to check on staff and clients and their safety.

If the fire is minor it may be possible to take corrective actions. These actions may include the use of the correct fire extinguisher. Fire extinguishers are colour coded to indicate their suitability for use, so therefore take care to ensure that the correct choice is made. A fire of hot wax, for example, may be smothered by a fire blanket. Do not attempt corrective action if it puts yourself or others at risk.

If possible, turn off any electrical or gas appliances before vacating the building and close the windows. Be aware of the location of all fire appliances, such as fire extinguishers and fire blankets. Most appliances do have guidance in their correct and appropriate use.

Fire Extinguisher Ratings

Ordinary Combustibles

Class A Extinguishers will put out fires in ordinary combustibles, such as wood and paper. The numerical rating for this class of fire extinguisher refers to the amount of water the fire extinguisher holds and the amount of fire it will extinguish.

A

Ordinary Combustibles

Flammable Liquids

Class B Extinguishers should be used on fires involving flammable liquids, such as grease, gasoline, oil, etc. The numerical rating for this class of fire extinguisher states the approximate number of square feet of a flammable liquid fire that a non-expert person can expect to extinguish.

B

Flammable Liquids

Electrical Equipment

Class C Extinguishers are suitable for use on electrically energized fire. This class of fire extinguishers does not have a numerical rating. The presence of the letter "C" indicates the extinguishers agent is non-conductive.

C

Electrical Equipment

Class D Extinguishers are designed for use on flammable metals and are often specific for the type of metal in question. There is no picture designator for Class D extinguishers. These extinguishers generally have no rating nor are they given a multi-purpose rating for use on other types of fires.

D

Combustible Metals

Multi-Class Ratings

Many extinguishers available today can be used on different types of fires and will be labelled with more than one designator, e.g. A-B, B-C or A-B-C. Make sure that if you have a multi-purpose extinguisher it is properly labelled.

This is the old style of labelling indicating suitability for use on Class A, B, and C fires.

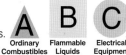

A
Ordinary Combustibles

B
Flammable Liquids

C
Electrical Equipment

This is the new style of labelling that shows this extinguisher may be used on Ordinary Combustibles, Flammable Liquids, of Electrical Equipment fires. This is the new labelling style with a diagonal red line drawn through the picture to indicate what type of fire this extinguisher is NOT suitable for. In this example, the fire extinguisher could be used on Ordinary Combustibles and Flammable Liquids fires, but not for Electrical Equipment fires.

Figure 4.2 Types of fire extinguishers

Areas and cupboards containing flammable products should be marked with a hazard sign and care should be taken near such areas. A fire-fighting team should be informed, if possible, of these areas and the likely contents.

HANDLING STOCK

Stock, including retail stock, is what you as the therapist use in the process of providing a service. Without the appropriate stock available you may be prevented from undertaking the business activity.

You will receive stock that may be for retail sale or professional use, it may be consumable stock or small equipment. When receiving a delivery you may be asked to sign to the effect that all goods have been received in prime condition. This should only be done if you have the authority to do so. Unless the package is opened, there and then, the document should be signed and noted to the effect that the goods were 'received and checked unopened'. Only sign if authorised by the company for which you work.

Do not, without prior permission from your supervisor, accept delivery of stock for other businesses, as once received the responsibility for its safe onward delivery may be transferred to your salon. Your salon may have specified times when it will receive stock – check this detail with your supervisor. Specified delivery times can reduce congestion and the necessity for a member of staff to be available to receive stock when they could be otherwise employed about the business.

A copy of the delivery document will be retained by the carrier as proof of delivery. Should the package(s) show any signs of damage it should not be signed for until checked fully – if in doubt, consult your supervisor. Goods delivered will normally be accompanied with a delivery note that should list all the items contained as well as indicating the number of packages. The delivery note will either be handed to the recipient of the delivery or be enclosed in the parcel(s). The goods should be checked as soon as possible following the delivery to ensure accuracy and that they are received in prime condition, at least within the time period allowed by the carrier.

Packages should be stored correctly. Information about correct storage procedures are often displayed on the outside of the package, particularly if the goods contained are of a fragile nature. Information provided on packaging will indicate:

l how many boxes may safely be stacked above each other, without damage to the contents or the person handling them

l arrows may indicate which way up the package should stand

l an umbrella sign indicates that packages should be kept dry

l a wine glass sign indicates that the contents are breakable.

Always follow the guidelines provided.

Packages should not be left at the salon's reception but should be moved to the stock area promptly. There may be particular areas designated for storing certain forms of stock, either stock of very high value or that which may be highly inflammable or toxic. Boxes left at reception become a risk, not only to security but also to health and safety. Move packages with care: do not lift over-heavy items and seek help or use specialised equipment; for example, a sack trolley. If you have to lift, ensure you lift correctly. Do not carry more than can be held firmly and do not allow your sight line to be obscured when moving stock,

TIP: Do not allow yourself to be pressurised into signing for the receipt of stock for which you do not have responsibility or if you are unable to check it in the time permitted by the carrier. Remember, once you have signed, you have accepted responsibility. The carrier may have a busy schedule but the purchaser of the stock has usually paid for the delivery service and is therefore entitled to receive a high-quality service.

TIP: Before accepting delivery of goods find out who in your salon has responsibility for this. If you are in any doubt about procedures, check with the responsible person before acting.

particularly when carrying stock up or down staircases. When placing stock items on a shelf do not over reach as you may fall and when using steps or a step up stool, do so only on a flat dry surface and once again avoid over reaching. Avoid lifting containers of corrosive liquids above yourself in case of spillage.

Once the delivery has been located in the appropriate area, typically the stock room, the contents should be checked. Most salons have a person specifically responsible for this. Packages should be opened with care and sharp implements for cutting tape or cardboard should be used with caution to avoid damage to the contents as well as to yourself. Always pay particular attention when unpacking retail goods as these packages must not be damaged since this may affect their saleability. Take care when dealing with damaged goods and wear protective clothing when handling broken containers – seek advice first from your supervisor. If this is not available, information may be obtained from the manufacturer if you are uncertain how to dispose of the product safely. If this information is unavailable contact the local environmental health officer.

Check the contents of the delivery for accuracy of goods and quantity and check this against the delivery note, which in turn is checked against the order to ensure that the delivery matches that which was requested. Watch for signs of damage to goods. This may be indicated by stained or damaged packaging and rattles from boxes, which may indicate breakage. All breakage or errors in delivery should be recorded and reported promptly to the distributor. Check the delivery note for guidance in notification procedures. If you are in any doubt, seek guidance from your supervisor or, if this facility is not available, contact the supplier direct and verbally notify the appropriate department and request guidance. Whenever you contact a company to notify them or request guidance, make a record of the conversation, the date, time, person spoken to and a brief resumé of the conversation. Store these notes with the delivery note.

Damaged stock is usually collected, 'uplifted', by the distributor. The goods should be packed securely and retained ready for collection. Ensure that a receipt is obtained for the package from the carrier.

Check what the goods received are and where they are labelled with sell by dates or use by dates make sure these are well within the date for sale. If you are in doubt about the shelf life of a product consult the manufacturer. Goods, once passed their sell by date should not be offered for resale to the public as they may have deteriorated in the packaging. The accepted stock rotation practice is to offer for resale or to use in stock the items which have been received earlier before using the newer stock. Therefore the old stock is drawn forward on the shelf and the new stock placed behind. This helps to reduce the risk of stock deterioration and is sometimes known as FIFO (first in first out).

In some cases goods may be 'out of stock' and this will be notified on the delivery note; it may indicate that the goods are to follow or that they should be reordered. Always inform the person in your salon who is responsible for these variations. They may wish to re-order from a different supplier or to order alternatives rather than wait.

As the goods are unpacked the packaging should be disposed of. This will reduce any hazard risk caused by obstruction or fire hazards caused by excessive volumes of combustible material. Take care to place used packaging in the refuse bin and do not store material under staircases, etc. Packaging can be flattened to reduce bulk. Be careful if burning packaging as much of this can produce toxic fumes and be highly inflammable. It is best to dispose through a commercial refuse collection agency. When

TIP: Some salons have rules relating to the delivery point of goods and may require all deliveries to be made to a delivery bay where they may be received rather that the customer reception. Find out your salon's procedure.

TIP: Take care when lifting heavy objects. Do not lift more than you can cope with safely. Always lift by bending your knees and maintaining a straight back; this will help to prevent back strain. If in any doubt, seek advice or assistance.

TIP: Many suppliers now use returnable packaging, which is designed to reduce the consumption of natural resources. In these cases store and return to the distributor promptly.

disposing of packaging that may have contained chemical leakage watch out for any subsequent reactions that may put people at risk; for example, hydrogen peroxide may self ignite and certain solvents can be highly inflammable. When dealing with chemical leakage always wear appropriate protective clothing.

Storing stock

As part of your salon's compliance with the Control of Substances Hazardous to Health (COSHH) regulations there will be guidance in the safe storage and use of products. Take care to comply with these and should an accident occur refer to the 'data sheet' for the product or the guidance provided.

Always store hazardous goods in the correct identified location; if you are uncertain, check this with your supervisor. Areas designated for the storage of hazardous substances will have appropriate hazard warnings clearly displayed and will be suitable for the storage of these items. Avoid storing next to each other any stock which may react should leakage occur.

In most cases the ideal storage conditions for stock, both for retail and for professional use, is in an area that is dry, dark and cool with an even temperature. Do remember that when using chemicals that have been stored in a cool environment they may be slow to react until they have warmed up. Allow additional time for this, particularly where the salon stock area may have been closed and cool for some period of time; for example, on a winter weekend.

Quantities of stock are often stored away from the retail display areas. These areas will normally be secure and entry will often be restricted to those who have responsibility for stock control. Records will be maintained of stock entry and exit and this may be reconciled with the salon takings to ensure that the products are producing the anticipated level of business income. It is usual for an appointed person to move stock from this area to a daily use area where stock levels will be maintained to enable the normal daily business activity. This will include the normal level of retail sales. It can be possible to forecast the anticipated level of business and therefore the required stock level from records of previous years' transactions. These records can be an essential tool in planning and forecasting stock levels for a business for any part of the trading year.

When storing stock the heavier items are usually placed low down on the stock shelves. It can be advisable to place stock that can be corrosive below eye level in case of accidental spillage. The storage facility must always be secure and safe. Shelving will be fixed to the wall to avoid tilting. When specialised facilities are required, for example a flame-proof cabinet for inflammable liquids, this should be supplied and appropriately labelled. In case of an emergency, a responsible person should notify the emergency services of the location of these risk areas. Retail stock is often located in a different area to that for professional use to avoid the accidental use of products.

YOUR PROFESSIONAL APPEARANCE

Your appearance will project an image to your client. This first impression can set the tone of your relationship with your client for the remainder of your professional relationship. The image of the beauty therapist is most often that of an efficient and knowledgeable expert with a professional

TIP: Remember that you have a responsibility not to put yourself or others at risk by your actions or omissions.

TIP: There may be local regulations relating to the storage of inflammable chemicals – check with your environmental health officer.

TIP: At all times avoid damage to product packaging, particularly for retail products.

concern about the way people look and feel. This will be reflected in the way that you present yourself. Many salons have a predetermined style of acceptable dress for work. This usually ensures that a corporate image is projected.

Clothing

Clean, easily maintained protective clothing should be worn when working in the beauty salon. This will protect you from damage or injury from spillages of products that you or others use and will also protect your client from contamination. It is most usual for this clothing to be light coloured, though this is not essential. To maintain standards of hygiene these protective garments should be worn only in the salon as this helps to reduce the risk of introducing infection and bacteria from outside. This clothing should be easy to launder and kept clean and pressed.

Regular laundering of protective clothing will not only maintain a level of personal hygiene but also remove spilt chemicals, some of which can be simultaneously combustible, that is, self-ignite.

Your shoes should provide support and protection. Your toes and the sides of your feet need to be protected from spillages and dropped items, particularly sharps. You will be standing for long periods of time during your working day so to prevent unnecessary fatigue and posture deformity your shoes should provide support and have heels which are not too high.

Figure 4.3 Correct dress for beauty therapist

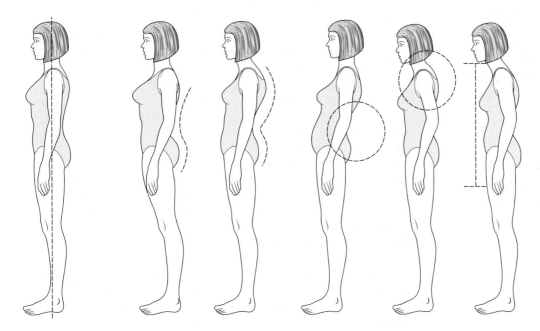

Figure 4.4 Good posture (left) and five defective postures

Jewellery

When working with clients you should remove all items of jewellery, particularly from your hands and arms. A wedding band can remain but should be covered with an adhesive plaster. When undertaking electrical treatments the wearing of conductive material such as jewellery can cause electrical arcing, that is, unpleasant sensations which may dangerously interfere with the treatment being provided. Jewellery may also scratch or mark your client, harbour bacteria or conduct heat to your client.

Hair

Your hair should be clean and secured way from your face and off your shoulders. Hair falling onto your face may obstruct your vision at crucial moments during a treatment. When working close to your client it can be unpleasant for the client to feel your hair falling onto their skin, this may also be unhygienic.

Make-up

A minimum amount of make-up should be worn by the beauty therapist. Unlike many businesses, you are able to market your expertise through your appearance. Therefore if you are promoting the sales or use of make-ups, it may be very appropriate to wear expertly applied, discreet make-up.

As you will be working close to your client you should be careful with the use of strong perfumes and scents. Strong scents can be unpleasant to the non-wearer, particularly in a confined space, and they may clash with the client's perfume.

While working with your client you should not wear any nail enamel. Levels of hygiene can be difficult to maintain if nail enamel is chipped and the nail enamel may also adversely react with products you are using in your client's treatment. Clients may also be allergic to false nails and nail enamel.

INSTRUMENTS AND EQUIPMENT

Whenever equipment is used on more than one client there is a risk of cross infection. To reduce this risk all items should be cleaned and, when relevant, sterilised between use. This includes not only small portable equipment, but also larger fixed equipment such as couches, shower areas, steam baths and sunbeds. In some cases, for example the couch, the contact area may be covered with a disposable material which is changed between clients; in other cases, for example nail nippers, the tool must be washed, dried and sterilised.

All equipment used on clients must be cleaned and sanitised immediately following their use. Equipment should always be left ready for use. Equipment left unclean may contaminate other equipment, as well as creating a risk to you and your colleagues who may accidentally come into contact with it.

If you identify equipment that is faulty you should report it to the person responsible in your salon and handle it according to the salon's regulations. Remember that should you knowingly use equipment which is faulty this can endanger both you and your client as well as you risking disciplinary action.

Equipment cleaning

Always consult the manufacturer's guidance before cleaning equipment. Some equipment may be cleaned using warm soapy water, by total immersion in water or wiping with a damp cloth. Electrical equipment should not normally be immersed or soaked in water and a damp cloth

TIP: All exposed open cuts or abrasions must be covered using a clean waterproof dressing.

TIP: Find out your salon's procedures for reporting faulty equipment and hazards.

TIP: Take care when using chemical sterilising liquid as some have a bleaching effect on clothes, some can irritate the throat if fumes are inhaled and some can cause allergic reactions.

may be more appropriate. Equipment that is best not made wet may be cleaned using a specialised cleaning agent, this is often a spirit.

Remember to consult the manufacturer's guidelines as damage caused by incorrect use and may incur considerable expense in repair. If in doubt, consult your supervisor.

Once cleaned, all items should be allowed to dry and then, if small, placed in a covered container to reduce the risk of recontamination.

Sterilisation

Sterilisation may be provided using chemicals, rays or heat (moist and dry). For sterilisation to be effective, items must be clean and dry before the process begins. Grease left on the surface can reduce the effectiveness of the processes and contaminate the sterilising product.

Chemical

There are a number of sterilising and sanitising liquids available. Some of these require dilution with clean water, others are used in their full strength. Always follow the manufacturer's guidelines in use and suitability of particular items.

Some products require the equipment to be placed in the solution and remain there for a period of time. When using this type of product it is important that the strength of the solution is maintained and that its effectiveness does not reduce over time. The manufacturer will usually provide guidance relating to the effective life span of the product. Care must be taken not to allow dust or other contaminating substances to enter the product as this can reduce its effectiveness. Manufacturers often produce specialised containers for their products. These usually have a protective lid which helps to reduce contamination, but do remember that if you fail to wash and dry the item before placing it in the solution this omission may cause contamination.

Some chemicals are applied to the equipment using a clean pad. Products areavailable for use with items of equipment that should not be immersed in a liquid. The moistened pad applies sufficient product to sterilise partially the surface being wiped. Do remember that those areas not touched by the chemical will not be sterilised.

A recent introduction is the aerosol sterilising spray. The spray is usually directed at the items and the product often remains on the item. Read the manufacturer's guidelines before use. Take care when disposing of empty or partially empty aerosol containers and do not store them near heat. Do note that some plastics can be adversely affected by the application of certain liquids.

Rays

Ultraviolet light cabinets may be used for sterilising. These are usually cabinets with reflective interior surfaces and a specialised electrical bulb which produces ultraviolet light rays. The light will sterilise those surfaces which are touched by the light rays. With this in mind, it is important to ensure that items in the steriliser are rotated so that all areas are treated. Avoid over filling the steriliser as this can prevent the light rays touching all the surfaces. Check the manufacturer's recommended guidelines for duration of light exposure. This method is unsuitable for the sterilisation of equipment that has gaps, grooves, hollows, etc. which may not be hit by the light rays. The effectiveness of ultraviolet producing bulbs deteriorates with time so do consult a specialist servicing agent for advice.

Figure 4.5 A range of sterilising equipment

❝TIP: For health and safety reasons do not expose your eyes to the ultraviolet rays of the steriliser.❞

Heat

Dry heat

Dry heat may be used to sterilise very small items that are not adversely affected by high temperatures. The glass bead steriliser is the most widely used technique of this kind in beauty therapy. The steriliser consists of a small heater with a container of small glass beads. The item to be sterilised is placed among the beads and the heater is switched on and allowed to reach its operating temperature. The glass beads conduct the heat around the object. Once the process is complete the steriliser must be allowed to cool fully before hygienically removing and storing the sterilised item. Care must be exercised as this technique uses high temperatures and consequently there is a risk of personal injury from burning. Never use this technique near flammable liquids and always use the steriliser on a non-inflammable surface. Always follow the manufacturer's guidelines on how to use the equipment, its suitability for sterilising particular items and the sterilising times.

Moist heat

Moist heat at high pressure is produced in the autoclave. The high pressure enables water to boil and produce steam at a much higher temperature than would otherwise be achieved in the beauty salon. This technique is suitable only for those items of equipment that are not adversely affected by heat and steam.

The equipment operates in a similar way to a pressure cooker. A small amount of water is placed in the autoclave and the equipment to be sterilised is placed in a container that is lowered into the autoclave, and will rest just above the water level. The lid is firmly fitted in place and then the machine is turned on. As the machine heats the water some steam loss will occasionally be noticed through the pressure release valve, but this will stop once the pressure builds. When the autoclave reaches its working temperature it is allowed to operate for the recommended period and then the heater is turned off. The lid must not be opened at this stage as this will cause a very sudden and dangerous escape of high-pressure, high-temperature steam. Allow the autoclave and its contents to cool then remove the lid, take out the sterilised items and store them ready for use. In some cases the machine is self-timing and/or regulating. This ensures that the autoclave operates at the correct temperatures and for an adequate time for effective sterilisation. Always follow the manufacturer's guidelines on correct use.

Remember that the outside surface of the autoclave can become very hot while in use and must be allowed to cool and the pressure within must fall before it is opened.

Sterilising

Some items of equipment, particularly if they are used to pierce the skin, must be disposed of hygienically. Electrolysis needles should be disposed of in a 'sharps' box. This is a container, usually sealed with a one-way entry flap, into which all blood contaminated or sharp items are placed. Arrangements are made with a specialist for these boxes to be regularly replaced and those removed are incinerated. This is a specialist job and should be undertaken only by an authorised specialist. The local environmental health officer can usually advise on this.

Electrolysis needles that are reusable must be carefully stored and identified so that they are used only with the same client. Between use they may be sterilised in a glass bead steriliser.

Products such as depilatory wax are best not reused. Some manufacturers indicate that hot wax can be reused. However, there is always a risk of cross contamination as it will have been in contact with a client's skin. The temperature required to sterilise may not be achieved in the waxing unit and therefore it is advised that all used wax be disposed of and the wax pot be cleaned and sterilised using a sterilising fluid.

WORKING WITH YOUR CLIENTS

The practice of beauty therapy is such that you are working near to your client on a one to one basis. The nature of the treatments is often confidential and discreet As a therapist you must always respect client confidentiality. Your client's records should be stored in such a way that only those eligible in the salon have access to them.

Confidential and personal information discussed while providing treatment should not be disclosed to others. Information that is relevant to the treatment and the salon should be recorded as stated previously.

For a number of treatments the relevant aspects of your client's medical history should be known and in some cases written consent/agreement by the client's doctor may be required. This information must be retained in an ordered and secure manner in the salon

Do not make false or over zealous claims about the beneficial effects of the treatments that you provide.

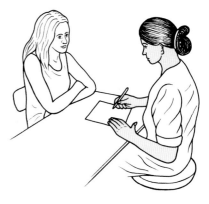

Figure 4.6 Well-kept record cards are essential

MONITORING

Your responsibility for monitoring health, safety and security within the salon will depend upon your level of management responsibility. All people at work have certain responsibilities irrespective of their position within the organisation. These responsibilities include:

- not intentionally putting themselves or others at risk by their actions
- to comply with the salons rules in relation to health and safety (provided that they are reasonable)
- to notify the responsible person of any identified faults with electrical equipment or installations
- to notify the responsible person of any contagious disorder that you may have
- to cover any open wounds or sores when undertaking electrolysis or skin piercing.

In order to comply with some of these personal responsibilities make yourself aware of who has responsibility for managing health and safety in your salon.

The beauty therapy industry has professional standards that are the norms of good practice. These include standards of personal hygiene - remember that you work in close proximity with your clients and therefore you should not tolerate personal body odour, breath odour or the scent of heavy perfumes etc. There are also standards of professional dress and appearance.

You may have supervisory responsibility within your salon that will often place additional roles of monitoring compliance of others into your job. You should confirm with your manager what responsibilities for monitoring you have and then devise a plan to undertake these.

In some cases monitoring may be informal, by observing – for example – the appearance of members of the team. Salon tidiness, clear access routes to fire exits, etc. will be done frequently but not necessarily at set times. In other cases, in particular when the monitoring relates to a legislative requirement, the monitoring may be more formal and will often be recorded. The frequency of monitoring may vary between each area but nevertheless there will need to be a routine. If you have five or more staff you will have a written Health and Safety Policy statement that may indicate checks and monitoring procedures.

Those items/areas, which will require checking and recording, include:

I display of appropriate health and safety information

I display of current certificate of employers liability insurance (may not require recording)

I electrical safety checking (PAT) of all electrical appliances used in your salon (including those belonging to members of staff) - this must be undertaken by a competent person at least once every year.

I first aid box contains adequate of the stated contents all of which are in good condition

I fire extinguishers are within the 'service period' (a specialist will be required to service or change extinguishers at set periods)

I all equipment provided for safety is in place and in good condition

I accident record book is in place and is correctly completed

I sharp's boxes are in place and collected at the determined intervals

I data sheets are available for all products used - the data sheet, available from manufacturers, will provide guidance in products' contents, the risk in their use and corrective actions to be taken in case of accident in their use.

It is advisable to maintain a record of these checks, indicating the date of the check, any findings/comments, name and signature of checker. If you delegate these tasks you are advised to spot check to ensure that the checks are undertaken as required.

As an employer you are required to provide the equipment for safe working as well as training in safe working practice. It is advisable to keep a written record that this training has taken place, so that in case of accident you can demonstrate that you have taken reasonable care to safeguard your employees.

Remember that all new staff will require an induction that should address all areas of health and safety. You may need to provide additional training for all employees when new products or equipment are introduced to your salon.

You may, as an employer, provide protective equipment for your staff to use; you must provide training in its use as well as ensuring that the equipment is used. You should not consider it an option that your staff can decide if they use protective equipment or not. If you have identified the need for its use it is your responsibility to ensure it is used at all times.

Do ensure that if day to day responsibility is delegated to members of your staff that they are fully aware of these and are provided with adequate support and time to undertake them.

RISK ASSESSMENT

As an employer you will be required to undertake an assessment of risk within your salon. These assessments must be undertaken regularly (recommend at least every six months or when working practice changes).

Health & Safety Risk Assessment

This is an assessment of any potential hazards in your salon. You should firstly review your salon for any potential hazards. Potential hazards may include low doorways, shelves that project outwards or trailing leads from electrical equipment. It can be helpful for more than one person to work together to do this. Having identified the risk you should determine who is at risk and prioritise the level of risk. Then identify what action can be taken to reduce the risk, who will do this and by what date. Remedial actions could include staff training, alterations or improvements to fittings and fixtures or hazard warning notices. Having identified a risk it is important to take a level of corrective or preventative action.

COSHH Assessment

The Control of Substances Hazardous to Health regulations require an assessment to be made of every substance that is used in the salon. A substance is considered to be hazardous if it may cause harm if inhaled, ingested, in contact with the skin, absorbed through the skin, injected into the body or enter the body via cuts.

All substances used should be assessed for potential hazard. Guidance in the potential hazard of a product will usually be given via data sheets available from manufacturers. It is your responsibility, as an employer to determine if there are any risks in the use or misuse of the substance in your salon. If a risk is identified you should determine who is at risk and what the risk is. Preventative or corrective action should then be taken to remove or reduce the risk. If the risk cannot be reduced and protection from the potential consequences cannot be provided you should make a decision as to whether the risk is acceptable. Remember that you may need to provide training for your staff in the correct use of substances. They should be informed of the risks and of remedial action to be taken.

Remember to update your COSHH assessment when new products are introduced to your salon and that new staff will need training in the safe use and corrective actions.

A chart, indicating potential hazards, corrective and remedial action which can be observed by all staff can aid communication of the message.

Remember that substances on their own may be quite harmless but when mixed together may become hazardous vapours. This should be taken into account in your assessment. These potential hazards should be taken into account when deciding that substances can be stored together.

SALON SECURITY

Every member of the beauty salon should accept a level of personal responsibility in the maintenance of salon security. The level of responsibility will depend on your salon requirements but it is reasonable for every employee to take reasonable care of the security of the salon.

The aspects of security at the most basic level will include the reporting of apparent breaches of security to the responsible person in the salon as well as avoiding risks to security by, for example, not leaving cash on display at an unattended reception or by not placing small items of stock or equipment in areas where they may readily be illegally removed. If you are in any doubt about your level of responsibility you should discuss this with your supervisor or manager.

As a supervisor or manager you will wish to provide guidance in good practice to your staff team. Setting an example by your own actions is a good starting point but you will need to formalise some systems and procedures, for example, cashing up, stock recording, storing clients' and staff's personal belongings and locking and unlocking the salon. Procedures can provide guidance to employees of the salon's preferred methods, these procedures in themselves may be development tools for staff. Systems will ensure that the procedures are used by the appropriate people. When reviewing your procedures you may consider the following guidance of help.

People: You may have people within your salon in vulnerable situations and you may need adequate security for entry to the salon. You may need areas within the salon with restricted entry at differing times. You may have areas to which only staff have access.

Possessions: You may be accommodating personal possessions of clients and staff. You may need a secure place to store client's clothing/possessions while undergoing treatment. Your salon may have a policy on the level of responsibility accepted for client's possessions. Staff will require space to store clothes out of which they have change. When providing client services. Staff may also be required to remove items of jewellery whilst working and will require a secure area for this to be stored.

Premises: Your salon, its fabric, fixtures and fittings. You may be required to ensure that the premises can be locked securely when not in use. Failure to take reasonable care of the security of the premises may invalidate any insurance protection.

Equipment: You may need to have procedures and systems for the regular maintenance of equipment in your salon. This may include regular checks for standards of cleanliness, damage or breakage and regular electrical safety checks by a qualified person. You may need to have procedures for reporting damage to equipment.

    Ensure that employees who use their own electrical equipment in the salon have this equipment electrical safety tested.

Tools: Must be maintained in a clean hygienic condition. You may need to ensure that there are adequate supplies of suitable equipment.

Stock: Stock rotation can help to reduce deterioration of stock. Stock must be secure and stored safely. Flammable stock must be stored appropriately. Regular and random checks on stock levels can support effective monitoring of stock use and loss.

    Avoid locating displays of stock in areas that may encourage theft: for example, near to public entrance ways, in areas where persons may remain unsupervised.

Cash: Avoid retaining high levels of cash on the premises. Remove large denomination notes and large cash volumes from the till at regular intervals. Ensure that monies taken in payment for services reconciles to the number of clients and the treatments provided.

    You may require formal procedures for the provision of

refunds, as well as the use of money from the till to make petty cash payments. Some salons restrict access to money to specified persons.

Monitoring security should be undertaken on a regular basis. The frequency may vary according to each individual circumstance. Random checks serve to ensure compliance on an ongoing basis. Checks should be recorded as evidence that reasonable care is taken.

SUMMARY

You will have determined, from the content of this chapter, the need to maintain a high level of quality in the service which you provide. There is legislation that safeguards your client's right to receive a service that is provided in a safe and hygienic environment. Your client will expect you to observe confidences and to be mindful of their well being. In some cases this will require referral to other specialists or consultation with the client's doctor.

Your colleagues have a right to expect you to respect their health and safety. As a supervisor you may have a responsibility to maintain the smooth operation of the salon and therefore you will be looking for efficient working patterns within the legislative framework.

FURTHER STUDY

1. Does your local authority have by-laws for regulating electrical epilation and ear piercing salons? If so find out what standards they set.

2. Check the evacuation procedures for your salon and calculate how you may best exit the salon in case of an emergency.

3. Check for any equipment that you may be expected to use in the salon. If there is any item that you are not confident in using, ask for guidance.

4. All electrical equipment should periodically be checked for electrical safety, and the date of this check indicated by a label attached to the equipment by the checker. Has all your equipment been checked? How often is the equipment checked in your salon?

5. Compile a booklet of instruction and guidance for sterilising equipment in your salon. This could be used when introducing new staff to your salon.

6. Draw a plan of your salon indicating any potential hazards to colleagues' and clients' safety. Indicate on the plan all exit routes and the location of any safety equipment including fire extinguishers, fire blankets, first-aid box and electrical circuit breakers (trip switches). This may be a useful tool when introducing new staff to the salon.

7. Survey the methods of sterilisation which are used in your salon. Check if they are effective and investigate if there are other procedures which may be more effective.

Review questions

1. Who, in a business, is responsible for undertaking a COSHH risk assessment?

2. Name the Act which requires the registration of electrolysis premises.

3. What is cross infection and how can it be prevented in the salon?

4. How should equipment be prepared before being sterilised?

5. How should a beauty therapist cover any exposed cuts or abrasions when working on a client?

6. What are the risks from spillages of liquid or powder on the floor?

7. What action should you take if you are to use a item of equipment with which you are unfamiliar?

8. Which type of fire extinguisher is most suitable for use on burning wax?

Facial treatments

This chapter introduces you to the facial electrical treatments that you will be able to add to your basic facial skills giving more variety to your facial treatments.

The practical approach of this chapter will enable you to assess your client's individual needs and through consultation with her, prepare a treatment plan.

The effectiveness of your specialised facials will largely depend on the frequency of your client's visits and a strict 'homecare routine' that should include the use of appropriate products to compliment the course of salon treatment.

Level 3

Elements

14.1 Assess clients and prepare treatment plans

14.2 Prepare the treatment room and client for electrical treatments

14.3 Treat clients using electrical equipment

13.1 Maintain safe working practices within the salon

11.1 Provide individual consultation services

CONTENTS

Introduction	66
Preparing a treatment plan	66
Vapour treatment	66
High Frequency	68
Vacuum Suction	71
Galvanism	74
Faradic type treatment (neuro-muscular electrical stimulation)	76
Microcurrent	78
Summary	79
Further Study	79
Review Questions	80

INTRODUCTION

Personal Appearance and Hygiene

As with all treatments that you perform, you must take pride in your appearance and personal hygiene. This will reflect your sense of responsibility to your profession.

PREPARING A TREATMENT PLAN

To establish the appropriate electrical services for your client you should, initially, identify their needs and concerns. A record card must be completed detailing the observations you make during the preliminary consultation.

Adopt a pleasant and sympathetic approach, demonstrating your ability to be tactful when diagnosing any treatable imperfections of the skin.

Ensure that you allow time to give a thorough consultation, do not rush your client or the treatment that follows. Consultation must be a two way process, giving your client the opportunity to voice the concerns about their skin and is essential for establishing their requirements and constraints.

An appropriate record card for this treatment would include:

l Personal details.

l Medical history.

l Skin type and condition.

l A checklist for contra-indications.

l Clients assenting signature.

l Treatment details in date order.

l Therapist's initials.

l Space of monitoring treatment progress and contra-actions.

l Purchases made/recommended.

l Homecare advice given.

Treatment may be given when your client agrees to the treatment plan and there are no contra-indications.

There are specific contra-indications to each treatment, as indicated in this chapter.

TIP: If the consent of your client's GP is required, obtain this in writing and attach it to your client's record card.

TIP: Remember consultation is a two-way communication process: give your client the opportunity to respond, and ask questions for clarification where necessary.

TIP: Wash your hands immediately before and after physical contact with your client.

VAPOUR TREAMENT

The vapour unit is an electrical appliance that produces a fine mist both with or without ozone and is used to assist deep cleansing the skin. Ozone is beneficial for it's anti-bacterial properties but research suggests that it is carcinogenic in large amounts and therefore it is no longer used in the training environment.

This unit may be free standing or portable, in which case it will need to be stabilised on a trolley or table top. This unit may be called 'Vapozone' or 'infrazone'.

Pre-heating the skin in this way has following effects:

l Induces perspiration (stimulates the sweat glands).

l Opens the pores.

l Warms the tissues.

l Increases circulation.

Figure 5.1 Application of vapour to the face

| Creates an erythema (redness).
| Rehydrates and softens the tissues.
| Stimulates the sebaceous glands.
| Deep cleanses.

Application of vapour

1. Ensure the steamer is filled to the required level with purified water (distilled or de-ionised). The use of tap water may cause a build up of lime scale that can block or congest the steam jets and reduce the efficiency of the heater. Check that the vaporiser is in a stable and secure position and that the electrical lead and plug are in good condition and not over stretched. If you are in doubt about how to use the appliance consult the manufacturer's guidelines or ask for guidance from your supervisor.

2. Using dry hands, switch the unit on, make sure that the nozzle is pointing away from your client. Switching the vaporiser on at this time will allow for it to heat ready for use.

3. Thoroughly cleanse your client's skin (this may be the face or body).

4. Ensure your client is not contra-indicated to this treatment. Check for the following:
   | hypersensitivity
   | vascular complexions
   | *Acne Rosacea*
   | sunburn or recent ultraviolet exposure
   | skin infections
   | inflammation
   | low blood pressure
   | Asthma or bronchial disorders
   | claustrophobia
   | cuts or abrasions.

5. While the steamer is warming up, describe to your client what you are about to do.

6. Protect areas of sensitivity with petroleum jelly and cotton wool. Ask you client to close their eyes and cover them with moistened cotton wool pads before directing the steam onto the client's face as they lie in a semi-reclined position.

7. Ensure that the distance between the vapour unit and the area being treated is correct to avoid over heating and time the treatment duration. A guide for this is provided below but always check the manufacturer's guidelines.

Skin type	Distance (cm)	Timing (minutes)
normal	56–64	10
oily	38–56	10–12
dry	38–56	10–12
sensitive	64	5–8

TIP: Take care not to trail electrical leads where they may cause a safety hazard.

TIP: Areas of minor sensitivity may be protected with cotton wool and petroleum jelly.

TIP: Equipment and materials must be clean and hygienic.

TIP: Ozone can be destructive in large doses. The presence of ozone in the atmosphere of the beauty salon should be monitored, as high levels can form a health risk.

TIP: When using the vapour machine, do not add anything to the water, for example chemicals, as this may cause the steamer to spurt liquid. This can occur as the chemicals may boil at different temperatures.

TIP: Any damage caused to electrical appliances should be reported to the person responsible for safety and maintenance as soon as possible and the machine taken out of use.

TIP: Move the vapour unit away from your client after use.

8. After steaming is completed, observe the skin's reaction and continue with the facial treatment.

9. After use, turn off and unplug the vaporiser. Clean the machine as soon as is practicable following the completion of the client's treatment.

High Frequency

This machine uses a High Frequency current that alternates at over 100,000 cycles per second. This current is not capable of stimulating muscle contraction but will produce a warming effect in the area it is used.

There are two techniques of application:

HIGH FREQUENCY

DIRECT   INDIRECT

Direct high frequency

The direct method is ideal for clients with greasy skin and over-active sebaceous glands. It is also beneficial for acne sufferers and the treatment of the 'T' zone on combination skin types. This technique uses a glass electrode that is gently moved over the skin's surface. The electrode has a metal connection and in its glass are small amounts of air, neon or mercury. When the electrode is placed firmly into its holder, the metal end makes contact with a metal plate inside the holder. Current flows from the machine, through and out of the holder and on through the electrode. The air or gas inside the tube ionises enabling the current to pass to the tissues directly under the electrode – sparking occurs when there is a gap between the electrode and the skin.

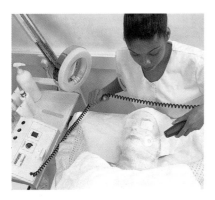

Figure 5.2 High frequency direct

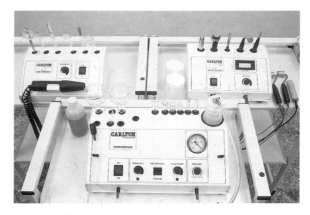

Figure 5.3 High frequency, galvanic vacuum suction equipment

Electrodes

These are inserted firmly into the holder:

I roller – may be used on the face and body

I neck – curved for the body's natural contours

I mushroom – general treatment and sparking of spots and pustules.

I saturator – convenient shape for your client to hold.

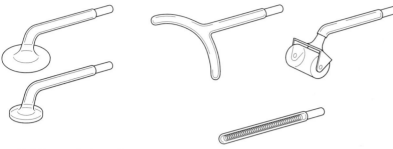

Figure 5.4 Types of electrodes

TIP: As with all treatments, always explain the sensation clearly to your client before commencement.

Effects

- produces heat
- increases metabolism promoting skin healing and therefore improving the skin's condition
- vasodilation, hence redness as blood flow is increased to the area
- soothing on the nerve endings due to the mild heat created, which in turn induces relaxation
- germicidal effect when the electrode is held off the skin, (approximately 0.5 cm) a spark is formed. The oxygen in the air becomes ionised and forms ozone which destroys bacteria and promotes healing
- drying effect – the pores constrict due to the stimulation of nerve endings. Ozone is also drying.

Application

1. Ensure that the equipment is on a stable base. Check the casing, cables and attachments for any apparent damage. If any damage is evident, the machinery should be taken out of action and reported to the person responsible for safety and maintenance in the salon.

2. Check your client for contra-indications, these are:
   - nervous disposition
   - Asthma
   - vascular skin conditions
   - skin infection (apart from acne, which may be treated with GP approval)
   - excessive number of metal fillings in your client's teeth, metal plates and pins
   - abnormal blood pressure
   - sinus problems
   - pregnancy
   - heart disorders
   - Diabetes
   - undiagnosed swellings
   - recent scar tissue (4–6 weeks)
   - loss of tactile sensation
   - migraine
   - previous exposure to ultraviolet light.

TIP: To avoid discomfort reduce intensity when working over bony areas.

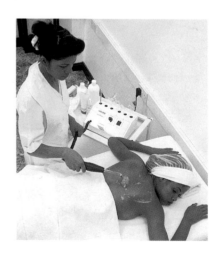

Figure 5.5 Direct high frequency to the back

3. If this is the first occasion that the treatment has been provided to your client explain the process to them in clear understandable terms.

4. Ensure your client's skin is free of grease by cleansing thoroughly and applying your medium. The medium may be talc or oxygenating cream (a cream which encourages the production of oxygen). Talc (unperfumed to reduce the risk of allergic reaction) will allow smooth movement of the electrode over the skin and absorb skin secretions; an oxygenating cream or emulsion will create a soothing effect. Gauze may also be required and may be placed on top of the face following the application of the appropriate medium (this will produce a gap between the skin and electrode to encourage production of ozone).

TIP: An oxygenating cream may encourage the production of oxygen.

5. With the machine turned off and with dry hands, firmly insert the selected electrode into the holder.

6. Switch on the machine, turning up the frequency control to the desired level, (follow manufacturer's guidelines) test that current is flowing by placing the electrode gently but firmly on the back of your hand. Turn the frequency control down and off and then re-sanitise the electrode, before applying the treatment to your client's face.

7. Place the electrode on your client's face and begin a rotary movement of the electrode. As you are doing this switch the machine on and gradually raise the intensity until a tingling sensation is experienced by the client.

8. Work in circular motion covering the whole area to be treated. Maintain contact with the skin at all times, spark where appropriate (not near eyes or mouth).

9. When the desired effect has been achieved, that is redness and warmth, gradually return the intensity control to zero, switch the machine off and then remove the electrode from your client's face.

10. Cleanse off any remaining medium from your client's skin with damp cotton wool pads.

11. Cleanse and sterilise the electrodes; specialised cleansing solution and sterilising liquids are available. Do not use high temperatures as the method of sterilising (see chapter 4).

12. When not in use, unplug the machine and cleanse it as soon as possible following the treatment.

Indirect high frequency

The indirect method is suitable for clients with dry, lined and dehydrated skins and involves your client holding an electrode called a 'saturator' (a metal tube or glass tube containing a coil) firmly in their hand while you massage the area using your hands. The current is transmitted through the client to the therapist's fingers and the fingers act as the electrode. Your client will feel the relaxing and warming effects of the treatment in the area being massaged.

TIP: Whilst carrying out the massage avoid breaking contact with the skin.

TIP: If your client suffers from clammy hands, apply a light dusting of talc to them before passing over the saturator.

Effects

I improves dry or dehydrated skin conditions

I stimulates circulation

I revitalises tired skins, improving fine lines

I induces relaxation.

Application

1. Check the machine, cables and electrode for electrical safety.

2. Ensure that your client is not contra-indicated (see those for direct method, page 69).

3. Ask your client to remove all jewellery. If your client is unable to remove a ring on their finger cover this with a plaster.

4. Thoroughly cleanse the treatment area and apply an appropriate medium – talc or oxygenating cream/emulsion.

5. With the machine turned off, insert the saturator into the holder and give it to your client.

6. Keeping one hand moving on the area massage gently, using the other hand turn the machine on and gradually increase the intensity until a tingling sensation if felt.

7. Massage using both hands for approximately 20 minutes.

8. When the desired effect has been achieved, remove one hand from your client and reduce the intensity to zero, keeping the other hand moving on the area.

9. When the controls are set at zero, remove the remaining hand from your client and retrieve the saturator that they are holding. Place this safely on the trolley.

10. Turn the machine off and unplug with your clean, dry hands. Clean the equipment as soon as possible following the treatment.

11. Continue with your treatment after removing any remaining medium. If you are to continue with manual massage you may leave the cream on.

TIP: Never perform any massage movement that breaks contact with the skin's surface, for example tapotement, as this may cause sparking, which may disturb your client's relaxation.

Vacuum suction

Vacuum suction is best given following a thorough cleansing and/or steaming. It uses negative pressure in a static or moving ventouse to stimulate blood and lymphatic circulation bringing about a deep cleansing of the skin and an increase in cellular activity. It is most effective if given as a course of treatment rather than a one-off and may be performed on the face and/or body.

A flexible strip of plastic tubing connects the ventouse to the suction unit, which is driven by a motor. When applied it sucks the tissue into a glass applicator for facial treatment or perspex or plastic cup (ventouse) for body treatment and is then taken towards the nearest lymph node.

TIP: If performing vacuum suction as a body treatment, it is advisable to pre-heat the body beforehand.

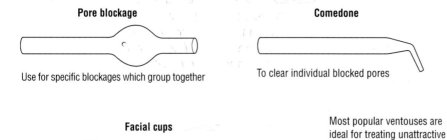

Pore blockage	**Comedone**	**Lymph drainage**
Use for specific blockages which group together	To clear individual blocked pores	Designed for fine lines and wrinkles to clear blocked pores and debris

Facial cups

27mm   21mm

Most popular ventouses are ideal for treating unattractive deposits e.g. double chin and for general massage of face and neck. The larger of the two for the back and body

Figure 5.6 Applicators and ventouse

Effects

- Increases circulation
- Erythema
- Oxygen and nutrients are brought to the area being treated
- Stimulates cellular metabolism
- Stimulation of lymphatic flow
- Removal of waste products from the area being treated
- Aids desquamation
- Lifts and loosens impurities
- Improves the appearance and texture of the skin
- Scar tissue may be softened

Application

1. Your client should be comfortable in a semi-reclined position, with the head of the couch slightly raised. Having checked for the specific contra-indications which are:

   - Acne
   - Broken capillaries/fine skin
   - Disorders and diseases e.g. scabies, psoriasis, herpes simplex
   - Sunburn
   - Hypersensitivity
   - Bony areas

TIP: When you have cleaned the ventouse cups place them in the steriliser, prior to and after use (see chapter 4).

TIP: In general the ventouse selected should be appropriate to the area to be worked on or should suit the purpose for which it is to be used, for example comedone removal.

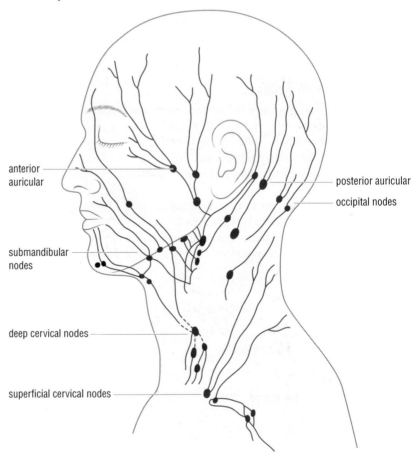

anterior auricular

posterior auricular

occipital nodes

submandibular nodes

deep cervical nodes

superficial cervical nodes

Figure 5.7 Lymph nodes of the face and neck

- Recent scar tissue (4-6 weeks)
- Abnormal blood pressure
- Bruising
- Broken skin
- Epilepsy (seek G.P.'s consent)
- Diabetes (seek G.P.'s consent)
- Heart condition (seek G.P.'s consent)
- Extremely loose skin
- Abnormal blood pressure
- Undiagnosed lumps or swellings (including glandular)
- Menstruation.

Thoroughly cleanse the area.

2. Apply a suitable medium to the area to be treated, usually this is a liberal covering of oil.

3. Ensure the glass or perspex ventouses are not damaged. Select the appropriate ventouse for your treatment. Test the machine on yourself first to ensure you are happy with the percentage of suction and the machine is in good working order. Sanitise the ventouse in hot soapy water or wipe over with antiseptic.

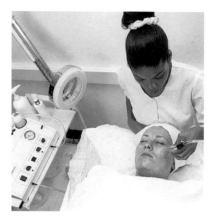

Figure 5.9 Vacuum suction to the face using ventouse

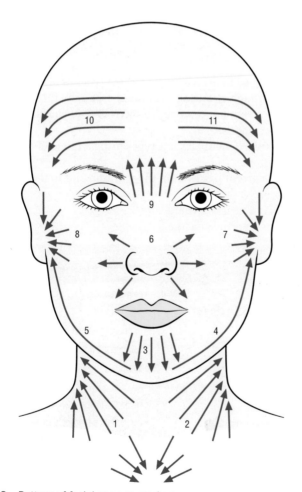

Figure 5.8   Pattern of facial vacuum strokes

4. You are now ready to apply the treatment to your client. Turn up the intensity with your free hand and apply the ventouse to the area to be treated. You may need to adjust the suction during the treatment as you move e.g.over bony areas. Ensure that your ventouse cup is never more that 20% full.
5. Always lift and glide the ventouse cup towards the nearest lymphatic nodes, stopping just before them. (see fig.5.7 and 5.8) Break the suction by depressing the tissues with your little finger or, if there is a release hole on the cup, by removing your finger covering it. This will reduce the suction and enable you to break contact with the skin without bruising.
6. In order to cover the area sufficiently it, is suggested that you carry out 6–8 strokes moving across the face or neck towards the nearest lymphatic nodes. This may be reduced if the area has been pre-heated.
7. The treatment usually takes 20 minutes, after which you should remove all the oil, unless you are following with manual massage.

GALVANISM

This treatment uses a direct current to produce a physical and chemical effect on the skin's tissues. There are two types of treatment:

GALVANIC TREATMENT

IONTOPHORESIS
Introduces water soluble substances through the skin

DESINCRUSTATION
Deep cleansing of the skin

Desincrustation will be indicated by most skins types as all skins can benefit from a thorough cleansing treatment, especially those suffering congestion as this treatment removes surface oiliness, blockages and helps to regulate oily secretions.

Iontophoresis, will benefit all skins types using a range of ampoules and gels.

To ensure that current passes from the galvanic unit to the skin, two electrodes are used:
Cathode – that has a negative charge.
Anode – that has a positive charge.

Action at the cathode when used as active electrode:	Action at the anode when used as active electrode:
• stimulates blood flow	• calms redness
• improves texture (refines and softens)	• firms tissues
• draws out impurities	• improves skin texture
• redness	• astringent action on the pores
• desquamates	• soothes
• removes grease (sebum)	
• destroys the acid mantle	• rebuilds the acid mantle
• alkaline reaction (sodium hydroxide)	• acid reaction (hydrochloric acid)

Application (Iontophoresis)

1. Prepare your client and ensure that they have removed their jewellery. Cleanse their skin and carry out sensitivity tests. Check for the following contra-indications:

TIP: The electrode used at the site of the area requiring treatment can be referred to as the 'active', the other electrode used to complete the circuit can be referred to as 'inactive' or 'indifferent'.

TIP: It is worth remembering that the basic principle of ions is 'likes repel and opposites attract'.

TIP: The resistance of the skin will initially be high but it is likely to decrease as the skin becomes moist. You may need to turn down the intensity of the current as the milliamp meter rises to prevent discomfort.

TIP: It is important to consider that natural body fluid resembles saline as it contains sodium chloride.

TIP: Ampoules and gels are available to assist this treatment and should be used according to the skin condition; for example, moisturising, cellulite and couperose complexion etc.

❙ open skin (cover minor lesions with petroleum jelly BP)

❙ diseases and disorders of the skin

❙ bony areas

❙ loss of sensation in the area requiring treatment

❙ circulatory disorders

❙ recent scar tissue, 4–6 weeks

❙ heart conditions

❙ metal plates, fillings, pace makers, IUD

❙ epilepsy (seek GP advice)

❙ diabetes (seek GP advice)

❙ pregnancy (seek GP advice)

❙ low blood pressure

❙ hypersensitivity.

2. Check the electrical equipment for any obvious damage, this should be reported and the equipment taken out of action.

3. Wash your hands and explain the treatment to your client (to include metallic taste and sensation).

4. Give your client the inactive electrode to hold (this may be protected by a damp sponge pad).

5. Select the appropriate water-soluble ampoule and apply it to the face and neck. Select the appropriate polarity on the machine (most iontophoresis ampoules and gels are positively charged and therefore a positive polarity should be selected) by following the manufacturer's instructions.

6. Raise the intensity of the machine and work over the area with the active electrode for 4–10 minutes.
   Note. Do not change polarity.

Application (Desincrustation)

1. Prepare your client as for Iontophoresis and give the client the indifferent inactive electrode to hold.

2. Prepare the active electrode; if using the black handled electrode with a round, flat surface, place damp cotton wool over the end of the electrode, secure with the captivating ring and apply desincrustation gel/solution of 1 per cent saline.

3. Place the electrode on the skin and ensure the polarity is set to negative.

4. Switch on the machine and increase the intensity as follows:

❙ Dry/sensitive skins = 0.15 ma

❙ Normal/combination = 0.20 ma

❙ Oily/problem = 0.25 ma.

Work over the face and neck for 8 minutes.

5. Turn down the intensity, switch the machine off and remove the active electrode from the skin.

6. Cleanse the ampoule/gel from the skin and replace the covering of damp cotton wool on the active electrode. Reapply the gel to the skin.

7. Switch the polarity to positive and reapply the current for 2 minutes, working over the face and neck using the above settings.

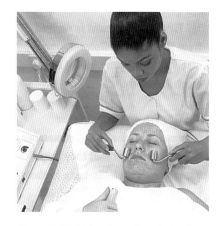

Figure 5.10 Using the roller electrodes

❝TIP: It is advisable to test skin with the hot and cold technique and sharp and soft technique.❞

❝TIP: Saline is an electrolyte (contains charged particles) and makes an effective conductor. Saline is used in the treatment of cellulite and for desincrustation.❞

❝TIP: An ampoule is a glass vial containing an electrically charged substance that must be opened immediately before application. The entire contents must be used in one treatment. Any remaining may be left on the skin after use.❞

❝TIP: If you are unsure about the polarity to use, test the contents of the ampoule's pH: if acidic, that is below pH 7, use the positive polarity; if alkaline, that is above pH 7, use the negative polarity.❞

❝TIP: To conduct the current from the electrode to the tissues of the body, a solution of 1 per cent saline is used. This may be made up by dissolving 1 teaspoon of salt in one pint of distilled water.❞

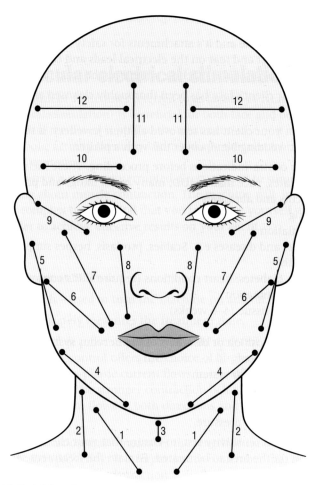

Figure 5.13 Facial faradic application

6. Cover the facial electrode with damp lint and test the machine on yourself to ensure that current is flowing.

7. Replace the lint and ensure that you have reset the dial to the 'off' position before placing the electrode on your client.

8. Place the electrode on the motor point of the chosen muscle (using the diagrams to help you in Fig.5.12 and 5.13) Warn your client as you increase the intensity control, until a muscle contraction is clearly visible.

9. After 6–8 clearly visible contractions, turn down the intensity control to zero and off during a 'rest' period.

10. Move on to the next muscle and repeat.

11. Treatment duration is usually 15–20 minutes.

Microcurrent

TIP: The basic principle of this treatment is to re-educate the facial contours.

NMES (Neuro Muscular Electrical Stimulation) is a non-surgical facial treatment that may be used to tighten and tone muscles, resulting in a smoother skin. This treatment must be provided in a course of at least 10 treatments for lasting results.

The current used is finely tuned to the level of the normal electrical exchanges which take place at the body, Micro current is considered more biologically compatible than any other electrical stimulation device.

Effects:

I Lifting and toning the facial contours.

I Reducing wrinkles resulting in a smoother the skin's surface.

I Refining skin tissue.

I Improving the skin's complexion.

I Heals scars and acne.

I Removes dark circles and puffyness from under the eyes.

I The skin appears more supple.

Application

1. Prepare the appropriate applicators, this may be with the use of single or duel tipped probes, rollers or pads (this will vary according to the manufacturer.

2. Complete a full consultation and check your client for contraindications. These will be as for all electrical treatments and in addition the specific ones stated below:

I Pacemaker

I Epilepsy

I Pregnancy

I Skin disease/disorders

I Metal pins/plates

I Recent scar tissue.

3. Cleanse and tone the facial area and blot the skin dry.

4. Select the appropriate electrode and apply gel to the face and neck.

5. Pattern of movements and machine settings will vary according to manufacturer's instructions (please refer to your training manual).

6. On completion of treatment, tone and moisturise.

SUMMARY

Electrical treatments will offer both variety to your clients facials and the confidence of more effective results. However, having read this chapter you will appreciate that electrical treatments need to be provided in packages of 6–10 sessions and some require your client to attend the salon as regularly as twice a week. Your preliminary consultation should assess how flexible your client can be regarding the frequency of their visits to the salon.

The treatments in this chapter will improve salon profitability and raise it's profile.

FURTHER STUDY

1. Draw diagrams to represent the following types of electrical currents:-

   a) interrupted direct current

   b) high frequency alternating current

   c) direct current.

2. Describe the effects of the following on electrical current

   a) a capacitor

   b) a rectifier

   c) a transformer.

TIP: Other areas for treatment include the breast, abdomen, thighs, buttocks, arms, hands and face.

TIP: Many salons offer a free introductory treatment to half the face to convince their client that it works instantly!

TIP: This treatment is totally safe and comfortable.

TIP: An ideal treatment for acne skin.

TIP: This treatment may also be used on the body in the treatment of cellulite.

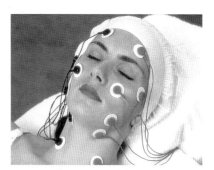

Figure 5.14 Electrical treatments

3. Research the main suppliers of non-surgical face lifting equipment and compare their prices and back up services.

4. Draw a diagram of the head and neck and label the following:-

   a) The lymphatic nodes

   b) The main facial nerves

   c) The major artery and vein that supplies the head and neck.

5. What do you understand by 1) AHAs and 2) 'Free Radical' damage?

6. List 6 pieces of advice that you could offer a colleague regarding the purchase of electrical equipment for their salon.

7. Draw and label the skull (front view and side view) .

8. Draw a chart to demonstrate your underpinning knowledge of the position and action of the main muscles of their face and neck.

Review questions

1. Give two reasons why you might record your client's personal details.

2. State three effects of vapour tretment and explain why prolonged exposure to ozone is a possible health risk.

3. Draw three electrodes that may be used in a high frequency treament and describe how they might be incorporated in to the routine.

4. State where you would stop your strokes when performing vacuum suction.

5. Describe the skin type that would benefit from desincrustation.

6. How does iontophoresis work?

7. List the uses and effects of NMES.

8. Explain why vapour treatment might be described as a heat treatment as opposed to an electrical one.

Figure diagnostics

This chapter aims to give you a foundation of knowledge on diet, figure analysis and exercise. You will find that these topics interrelate and will enable you to give constructive advice to your client as they embark on a course of body treatment

Elements

11.1 Provide individual consultation services

14.1 Assess clients and prepare treatment plans

15.1 Assess clients for body massage

17.1 Assess clients and prepare treatment plans

Introduction   82

Providing advice on dietary control   83

Figure diagnosis   85

Posture   89

Fitness   94

Summary   102

Further study   102

Review Questions   103

INTRODUCTION

Requirements of a healthy diet

It is essential for you to educate your client about the maintenance of a balanced diet. To do this you will need to acquire an understanding of nutrition and digestion.

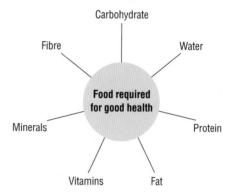

Figure 6.1 Nutrition web

Carbohydrates

These are necessary for energy and are available as starches and sugars. In excess carbohydrate will be converted to fat and stored until required.

Fats

These are needed for several purposes:

- protection of vital organs in the body
- to retain body heat
- to store in the form of fatty acids
- to provide energy.

Proteins

These are required for growth and the repair of body tissues and serve as a secondary source of energy. They are broken down during the process of digestion into amino acids.

PROVIDING ADVICE ON DIETARY CONTROL

Vitamins

Vitamins are required for health, in small amounts.

Vitamins	Function	Recommended daily intake	Sources
A (retinal)	Essential for growth, night vision, helps the body resist infection and promotes well being.	750 mg	Milk, butter, margarine, green and yellow vegetables, especially carrots, broccoli and spinach, and fruits.
B1 (thiamin)	Enable liberation of energy from food, calms and soothes the nervous system.	1.2 mg	Whole grains, peanuts, hazel nuts, dried peas, bran, cabbage, kidney, liver and potatoes.
B2 (riboflavin)	Enables liberation of energy from food. Needed to breakdown carbohydrates, oxygenating cells and maintains healthy tissue.	1.6 mg	Eggs, cottage cheese, cereals, milk, chicken, liver, beans and nuts.
B3 (niacin)	Reduces cholesterol, regulates blood sugar and aids circulation.	18 mg	Eggs, fish, meat, liver, nuts and whole grains.
B5 (pantothenic)	Metabolism of fats and carbohydrates. Aids immune system, anti-stress and increases energy.	Not known	Brown rice, nuts, mushrooms, beans, vegetables, liver, kidney and yeast.
B6 (pyridoxine)	Metabolism of protein, reduces fluid retention. Anti-stress, maintains hormones and nerves.	Not known	Green leafy vegetables, salmon, liver, beef, whole grain products and meat.
B1 (cyanocabakmin)	Required for the manufacture of red blood cells and nerve function.	2 mcg	Dairy products, fish, oysters, pork, beef and liver.
Folic acid	For the manufacture of blood cells, helps the body to use iron and maintain blood volume. Very important during pregnancy when the body requires more.	300 mcg	Milk, orange juice, broccoli, eggs, mushrooms and dark leafy greens.
Vitamin C (Ascorbic Acid)	Helps the body resist infection, prevents ulcers, healthy gums, enables the body to absorb iron. Maintains cementing substance between cells, healing of wounds.	30 mg	Citrus fruit, green vegetables, red and green peppers, tomatoes and black currants.
D (choleoql ciferol)	Necessary for the absorption of calcium, essential for healthy life. Promotes health in bones, teeth and nervous system.	2.5 mcg	Fish liver oils, fatty fish, margarine, exposure to sunlight.
E (tocopherol)	Keeps blood flow smooth. Antioxidant protects fatty tissues and cell walls.	Not known	Vegetable oil, butter, eggs, tomatoes, almonds and peanuts.
K	Important for blood clotting process, prevent haemorrhaging.		Dark greens, soya beans, eggs, yoghurt, cauliflower and wholewheat.

Minerals

Minerals are also required for health.

Minerals	Effects	Source
Iron	Manufactures haemoglobin, carries oxygen to the blood and stimulates the cells.	Beetroot, wheat germ, eggs, spinach and broccoli.
Calcium	Required for healthy teeth, bones, muscles and nerves. It is greatly reduced following the age of 45.	Cheese, milk, egg yolk and shellfish.
Phosphorus	Works well with calcium and vitamin D and is essential for maintaining healthy teeth and bones. It is found in the cells of the body.	Milk, cheese, seafood, bananas, avocado, pears, dried apricots and stewed prunes.
Magnesium	Promotes metabolism and enables the body to absorb protein and metabolise fats and carbohydrates.	Avocado, pears, nuts, green leafy vegetables and lentils.
Zinc	For the growth of brain and nerves, promotes healing.	Eggs, nuts, onions, shellfish, sunflower seeds, wheatgerm, bran
Iodine	Necessary for the development of the hormone thyroxin.	Watercress and seafood.

Other essentials

Trace elements are necessary for many of the body's natural processes; for example, digestion. Trace elements include fluorine and zinc.

Fibre is vital for the digestion as it stimulates peristalsis. It bulks out the food taken in encouraging the person to feel satisfied and full.

Water – ideally we should drink up to eight glasses of water a day as it assists elimination of waste products from the body and assists hydration of cells and maintenance of health.

TIP: Peristalsis is the movement of food through the intestine.

Contra-indications to dieting

- clients who are under 18 years of age or over 70
- clients under medical supervision
- severe obesity
- anorexia
- pregnancy
- food intolerance
- clients already undertaking a medically prescribed diet.

General diet advice for your client

- to enable your client to function healthily they require approximately 1200K calories per day
- avoid adding salt to meals
- increase fibre in order to stimulate peristalsis and promote a healthy digestive tract
- exercise regularly, three times a week for at least twenty minutes

I reduce the intake of foods containing animal fat

I reduce intake of fat, animal protein and sugar.

To be effective, set realistic goals for your client when changing their eating habits, as these changes must be for life. Set targets of 2.5 lb loss per week; this will ensure a gradual weight loss. Educate your client in exercise so that they may appreciate the notion of energy input versus energy output. Any plan must be nutritionally balanced.

TIP: Abduction = draw limb away from the middle line of the body. Adduction = draw limb towards the middle line of the body. Flexion = bending a limb or joint. Eversion = turn. Supination = facing upwards. Pronation = facing downwards.

FIGURE DIAGNOSIS

Name of muscle	Position	Origin	Insertion	Action
Muscles of the front of the leg				
Extensor group	Front and lateral side of the lower leg	Lateral side of the Tibia and Fibula	Phalanges	1. Dorsi flexion of foot at ankle joint 2. Extension of toes
Peroneal muscles 1. Peroneus Longus 2. Peroneus Brevis (lies beneath Peroneus Longus)	Lateral group of muscles of lower leg	Fibula	Tarsals, fifth metatarsal and crosses sole to first metatarsal	Plantar (sole of foot) flexion and eversion of foot
Quadriceps 1. Rectus Femoris 2. Vastus Lateralis 3. Vastus Medialis 4. Vastus Intermedius	Group of four muscles Front of the thigh	Front of Ilium (1) and greater trochanter of the femur (2,3,4)	Tubercle of Tibia via Patella	1. Extension of the leg at the knee joint (as running, cycling, jumping, kicking a ball) 2. Rectus Femoris flexion at hip joint only
Sartorius	Long strap-like muscle crossing the front of the thigh diagonally	Spine of Ilium	Medial side of the Tibia	1. Flexion, abduction and outward rotation at the hip joint 2. Flexion at knee joint (as sitting cross legged)
Adductor Group 1. Abductor Magnus 2. Abductor Longus 3. Abductor Brevis Gracilisl	Medial side of the thigh Innermost thigh muscle	Ischium and Pubis Ischium and Pubis	Shaft of Femur Tibia	Adduction and outward rotation of the thigh at the hip joint 1. Adduction, flexion and inward rotation of the thigh at the hip joint 2. Flexion at the knee joint
Tensor Fascia Lata	Small muscle at the upper side of the thigh. Joins into a long fibrous aponeurosis Fascia Lata at the side of the thigh to lower leg	Iliac Crest	Fascia Lata	Abduction, flexion and inward rotation of the thigh at the hip joint
Tibialis Anterior	Front of the lower leg	Upper two-thirds of the Tibia Lateral side	Tarsals and 1st Metatarsal	Dorsi flexion and inversion of the foot (used in walking pattern)
Muscles of the buttocks				
Gluteus Maximus	Most superficial and largest muscle of the group. Crosses the back of the hip	Iliac Crest and Sacrum	Greater trochanter of Femur	1. Extension of thigh at hip joint 2. Raises trunk from a stooping position 3. Maintains erect posture
Gluteus Medius	Lies in front and partly beneath Gluteus Maximus	Iliac Crest	Greater trochanter of Femur	Extension, abduction of thigh and medial rotation at the hip joint
Gluteus Minimus	Lies completely under the Gluteus Medius	Iliac Crest	Greater trochanter of Femur	Abduction and medial rotation of thigh at the hip joint

Name of muscle	Position	Origin	Insertion	Action
Muscles of the back of the thigh				
Hamstrings 1. Biceps Femoris 2. Semi tendinous (middle muscle of the group) 3. Semimembranosus (innermost muscle of the group)	Back of the thigh	Ischium	Fibula (Biceps femoris only) Tibia (other 2 muscles only)	1. Flexion of the leg at the knee joint, e.g. walking 2. Extension of the thigh at the hip joint 3. Aids inward and outward rotation
Gastrocnemius	Forms the bulk of the calf muscle. Back of the lower leg	Lateral and medial sides of the Femur (by 2 heads)	Calcaneum by the tendon of Achilles	1. Flexion of the knee 2. Plantar flexion of foot at the ankle joint (provides a 'push off' during walking and running)
Soleus	Back of the lower leg under Gastrocnemius	Tibia and Fibula	Calcaneum by the tendon of the Achilles	1. Aids Gastrocnemius therefore plantor flexion 2. Maintains balance
Flexor group	Deep group of muscles which lie under Soleus on the medial side of the lower leg	Tibia and Fibula	Tarsal, metatarsal and phalanges	1. Plantar flexion and inversion of the foot at the ankle joint 2. Flexion of the toes
Muscles of the foot				
Lumbricals and Interossei	Small deep muscles on the sole of the foot.	The muscles lie in both medial and lateral groups		Their action is to maintain the arches of the foot, and to propel and push the body forwards in walking
Muscles of the chest				
Pectoralis Major	Superficial muscle of the chest. Supports the mammary glands	Clavicle Sternum upper 6 ribs	Bicipital groove of Humerus	Adduction, flexion and inward rotation of the arm at the shoulder joint
Pectoralis Minor	Lies under the Pectoralis Major	3rd & 4th ribs	Scapula	Pulls the shoulder downwards and forwards as in slouching
Serratus Anterior	Side of the chest wall	Upper 8 ribs	Medial border of the scapula (muscle passes under the Scapula)	Abduction of the arm and rotates the Scapula forwards during punching movements
Intercostal Muscles	Eleven pairs. Lie between the ribs and forms the wall of the rib cage	Inferior border of one rib above	Superior border of next rib below	Muscles of respiration. Pulls ribs upwards and outwards to increase diameter of thorax during inspiration (both anteroposterior & lateral diameters)
Muscles of the abdomen				
Diaphragm	Dome-shaped muscle which divides the thorax from the abdomen (there are 3 openings to allow the passage of the oesophagus, aorta and inferior vena cava)	Sternum, lower 6 ribs, 1st, 2nd and 3rd Lumbar vertebrae	Tendon, known as the central aponeurosis	Muscle of respiration increases vertical diameter of the thorax during respiration
Rectus Abdominis	Front wall of the abdomen. Divided vertically into 2 parts by fibrous tissue – Linea Alba	Pubis	Sternum and lower ribs	1. Flexion of the spine and therefore bends the trunk forwards 2. Helps when lifting the legs from a lying position
External Oblique (2 muscles either side of the body)	Forms the waist. Fibres run downwards and forwards	Lower 8 ribs	Iliac crest and Abdominal Aponeurosis*	1. Flexion of the trunk forwards when working together 2. When one muscle is working side flexes trunk to the same side 3. When working with opposite external oblique muscle causes rotation of the trunk

Name of muscle	Position	Origin	Insertion	Action
Transversus	Deepest muscle of the abdominal wall. Muscles fibres lie at right angles to the rectus abdominus	Iliac crest, Lumbar fascia, Lower 6 ribs	Sternum and into the Abdominal Aponeurosis	Aids all other abdominal muscles and protects the internal organs
Muscles of the neck				
Platysma	Superficial muscle front and sides of the neck	Fascia on the front of the chest	Lower border of the mandible and depression of the chin	Depresses the lower jaw
Sterno-cleido mastoid	Sides of the neck	Sternum and clavicle (by 2 heads)	Mastoid process and occiput	1. Side flexion of the head the same side 2. Flexion of the head used together 3. Rotation of the head to the opposite side
Muscles of the arm				
Deltoid	Muscle of the shoulder. Triangular in shape, gives rounded shape to the shoulder	Scapula and Clavicle	Humerus	1. Main action is to abduct the arm at the shoulder joint 2. Anterior fibres flex the arm at the shoulder joint 3. Posterior fibres extend the arm at the shoulder joint
Biceps	Front of the upper arm	Scapula by 2 tendons, 1 of which passes through the shoulder joint	Tuberosity on the Radius	Flexion and supination of the forearm
Triceps	Back of the upper arm	By three tendons, 1 to the Scapula and 2 to the Humerus	Process of Ulna	Extension of the forearm at the elbow joint
Pronator Teres	Crosses the front forearm obliquely	Common flexor tendon of the Humerus (medial epicondyle)	Lateral outside surface of the Radius	Pronation of the forearm (turns the palm of the hand downwards)
Flexor Group	Small muscles at front of the forearm	Common flexor tendon	Metacarpals and phalanges	Flexion, adduction, abduction of the wrist joint and fingers
Extensor Group	Back of the forearm	Common Extensor Tendon (lateral epicondyle of Humerus	Metacarpals and Phalanges	Extension, adduction, abduction of the wrist joint and fingers
Muscles of the hand				
Thenear Eminence	Ball of the thumb			Small group of muscles which make up the fleshy ball of the thumb
Hypothenar Eminence	Base of little finger			Small group of muscles which make up the fleshy mass at the base of the little finger
Lumbricals and Interossei	Minute muscles lying between the metacarpal bones			Used for precision and fine delicate movements of the hand and fingers
Muscles of the back				
Trapezius	Lies below the shoulder and upper part of the neck	Occiput, cervical and thoracic vertebrae	Clavicle and Scapula	1. Raises the shoulders as in shrugging 2. Rotates the Scapula outwards when raising the arm 3. Aids extension of the head
Latissimus Dorsi	Large back muscle which lies on the sides of the back	Scapula Lower 4 ribs Thoracic vertebrae	Bicipital Groove of Humerus (tendon twists upon itself)	Adduction and inward rotation of the arm. Raises the body towards the arm used in climbing

Name of muscle	Position	Origin	Insertion	Action
Errector Spinae	Lies on either side of the spine	Ribs, Lumbar vertebrae, Iliac crest, Sacrum	Occiput, Mastoid Process, ribs and vertebrae	1. Extension of the spine and neck 2. Maintains erect posture
Quadratus Lumborum	Back of waist. Forms posterior wall of the abdomen	Iliac crest	12th rib and upper 4 lumbar vertebrae	1. Extension of the spine in the lumbar region 2. Side flexion of the trunk to the same side of the lumbar region
Iliacus Psoas (Ilio-psoas)	Internal muscle of the pelvis. Forms back of the abdominal wall	12th thoracic and lumbar vertebrae (Psoas) Ilica crest, front of scarum (Iliasus)	Femur	1. Flexion and inward rotation of the hip joint 2. Flexion of the spine (as lying to sitting)

*The Abdominal Aponeurosis is a flattened sheet of tenuous fibres. Laterally it is in three layers attached to the external, internal oblique muscles and the transversus. Medially, the fibres are interwoven to form a strong tendinous bank called the Linea Alba. This extends from the xiphoid process to the pubic symphysis. The lower edge of the aponeurosis is thickened to form the Inguinal ligament which extends from the Iliac to the pubic bone.

The breasts

The breasts are composed of fat and fibrous and glandular tissue and are influenced by the hormones oestrogen and progesterone. Their main function is for breast feeding.

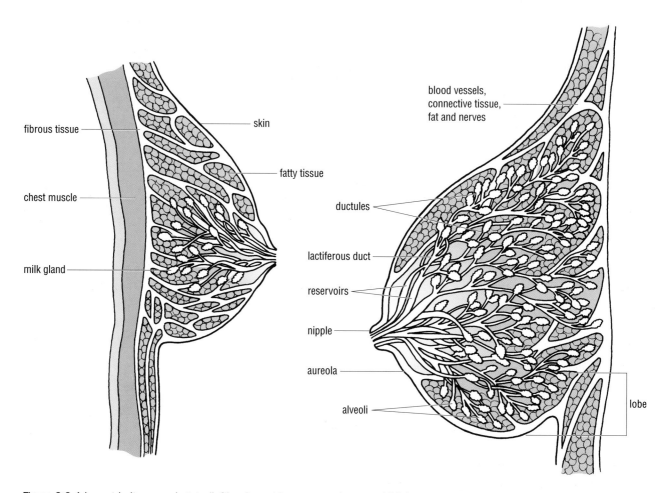

Figure 6.2 A breast in its normal state (left); a breast in a pregnant woman (right).

Posture

This may be defined as the platform on which all movement is superimposed and constantly adapts into which function is being performed. Posture may be:

I inactive – in a position of complete rest

I active:

a) static postural muscles help to support joints providing stability

b) dynamic postural muscles constantly adapt to help activities

I efficient – a balanced posture

I inefficient – an imbalanced posture.

Posture varies from person to person and there is no true measure of good posture but if you would like to analyse a client's posture use a plumb line as a guide. This represents an imaginary lateral line passing through the body

TIP: Position your client so that you may observe the anterior, posterior and lateral views.

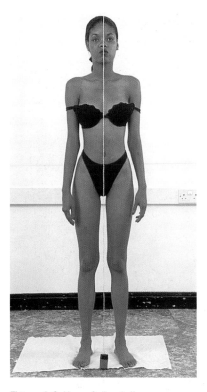

Figure 6.3 Use of plumb line
– anterior

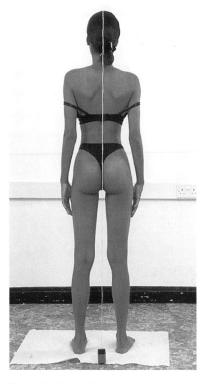

Figure 6.4 Use of plumb line
– posterior

Figure 6.5 Use of plumb line
– lateral view

Identification of good posture

I well balanced position when standing

I body weight equally distributed

I abdomen pulled in

I chest naturally elevated, arms loose at the side of the body

I head held up

I natural curvature to the back.

Assess the client's posture noting any deviations.

Recognising common posture defects

Defect	Description	Causes and complications
Kyphosis	Increase in thoracic curve	Tight pectorals, inherited, drooped breasts
Lordosis	Exaggerated lumbar curve (hollow back)	Anterior Pelvic tilt, shorter hip flexars, backache
Scoliosis	Lateral curve of the spine	Alters total body alignment. Different leg lengths, uneven shoulders and many more
Round shoulders	Shoulders brought forward (usually accompanies Kyphosis)	Tight Pectorals
Pelvic tilt	Hips sway forwards, backwards or sideways	Alters total body alignment
Flat feet	Absence or deformity of the arch of the foot	Problems in walking, discomfort when standing for prolonged periods
Knock knees	Knees bump together when walking, running etc.	Puts a strain on the hips and muscles of the legs

Common figure faults

| Poking chin
| Fat deposits under chin
| High shoulders (over tense posture)
| One shoulder higher than the other
| Rounded shoulders
| Dowager's Hump
| Adipose deposits Biceps and Triceps
| Poor muscle tone on Triceps
| Bust and chest (muscle tone)
| Ribcage (rotation to the side)
| Spine
  – Kyphosis (doreal spine)
  – Lordosis (lumbar spine)
  – Scoliosis
| Adipose deposits on the upper back beneath the shoulder blades
| Waist and muscular tone and adipose deposits
| Abdomen – Adipose deposit, weak abdominal muscles
| Buttocks
  – Adipose deposit
  – Poor muscle tone (dropped bottom)
| Pelvic tilt – increased or decreased
| Legs
  – muscular tone
  – adipose deposits
  – cellulite
  – knock knees
  – bow legs

– hyperextended knees
– hyperflexed knees
– uneven leg lengths.

❙ Ankles – fluid retention (poor circulation)

❙ Feet – flat feet.

Figure postural consultation

A suggested figure consultation plan may include:

❙ weighing and measuring (see record card)

❙ posture check using the plumb line

❙ calculating the percentage of body fat

❙ fitness testing (optional)

❙ analysis of your client's diet and lifestyle.

TIP: Allow at least 30 minutes to carry out a figure analysis consultation.

Body types

There are three main body types. It is useful to remember that most people do not fall into one category but are a combination of body types.

❙ Ectomorph – slender, tall, minimum of fat and muscle. Defined cervical and thoracic curves. Long bones, slim pencil shape.

❙ Mesomorph – muscular build, well developed shoulders and slim hips. Strong limbs.

❙ Endomorph – plump, rounded heavy body. Soft, pear-shaped figure. Padded contours and fatty deposits stored all over.

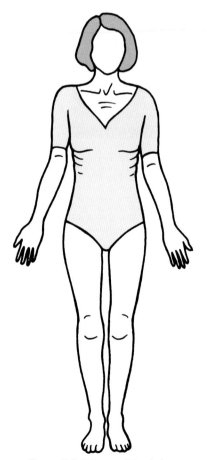

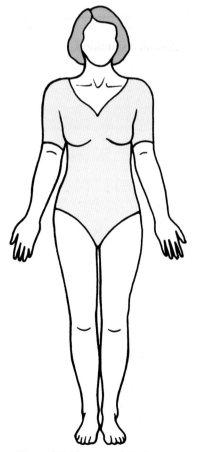

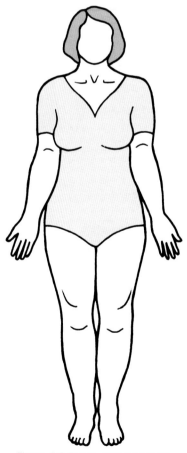

Figure 6.6 Ectomorph body type   Figure 6.7 Mesomorph body type   Figure 6.8 Endomorph body type

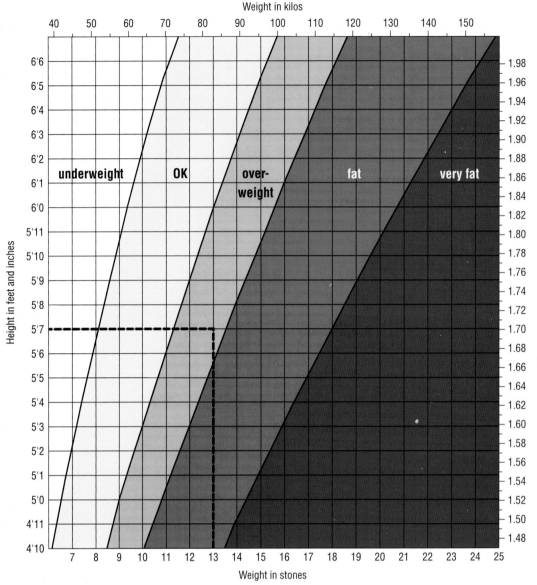

Figure 6.9 Height and weight chart for adult males and females

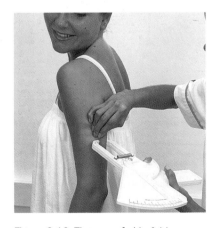

Figure 6.10 The use of skin fold callipers

Figure analysis

Obesity

People who are extremely overweight are more likely to suffer from conditions such as heart failure, increased blood pressure, diabetes and respiratory problems. It is possible to measure the percentage of body fat in two ways: with skin-fold callipers, which may be used in the beauty salon, or by counting fat cell number and size, which would be carried out by a medical physician.

Skin-fold callipers

The skin is measured in four areas: triceps, suprailliac, biceps and subscapular.

Procedure

1. Take the skin between the thumb and forefinger and gently apply the callipers.
2. Having taken the measurement, release the callipers and note the measurement.
3. The sum of these four skin folds can be converted to a percentage of body fat using the table in Purnin and Wormersley (1974).

Underweight

If you calculate that your client's percentage of body fat is less than 17 per cent body fat (12 per cent if male) then they would be classed as lean. This may not pose any medical implications for your client but you should be alert to Anorexia. This disorder involves a phobia regarding weight control and the individual refuses food. It can be extremely distressing for the suffer's family and friends and symptoms include:

▎ failing to eat for long periods

▎ vomiting, often self-induced

▎ loss of weight – obvious/considerable

▎ menstrual cycle ceases

▎ may attempt to conceal weight loss

▎ may follow male sexual characteristics.

> **TIP:** In men the body should not be composed of more than 20 per cent fat; in women the figure is slightly higher at 30 per cent. Any calculation above these figures is considered obese.

> **TIP:** When purchasing skin-fold callipers, refer to the manufacturer's guidelines for the location of the four areas in detail.

> **TIP:** Take care to only grasp skin and not muscle when taking these measurements.

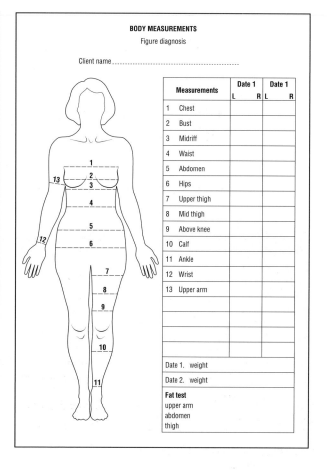

Name		Tel (home)	Tel (work)
Address			
		Post code	

Doctor	Tel	Date of birth
General health – good/poor	Smoke	Drink
Medical conditions under treatment		
Medical history	No. of children	Ages
	Asthma	Diabetes
	Epilepsy	Heart/circulatory conditions
	Bone/joint problems	
Operations/illnesses and dates	Hysterectomy	Caesarean
	Others	Digestive problems
Body condition	Overweight	Underweight
	Muscle tone	Body type (proportions & shape)
	Unusual markings	Spine
	Local contra-indications	Fat areas
General treatment plan	General reduction	Specific reduction
	Massage & relax	Cellulite
Recommended treatments/general comments/advice		

Therapist signature .... Date ....

BODY MEASUREMENTS
Figure diagnosis

Client name ....

Measurements	Date 1		Date 1	
	L	R	L	R
1 Chest				
2 Bust				
3 Midriff				
4 Waist				
5 Abdomen				
6 Hips				
7 Upper thigh				
8 Mid thigh				
9 Above knee				
10 Calf				
11 Ankle				
12 Wrist				
13 Upper arm				

Date 1. weight
Date 2. weight

Fat test
upper arm
abdomen
thigh

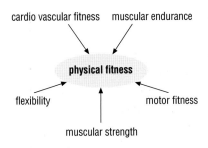

Figure 6.11 The components of fitness

FITNESS

What is fitness?

Fitness may be defined as one's ability to perform daily tasks energetically without feeling tired and having enough energy left to enjoy leisure time and to meet unforeseen emergencies; for example, running for a bus.

Cardio vascular fitness = the ability to breathe in, transport and utilise oxygen.

Muscular endurance = the continued performance of a single muscle or group of muscles.

Motor fitness = co-ordination, power, speed, agility and reacting quickly.

Muscular strength = the ultimate force with which a muscle or muscle group can generate against a resistance.

Flexibility = the range of movement with a joint.

Before embarking on any type of exercise check your client for contra-indications:

- abnormal blood pressure
- heart/circulatory disease
- chest conditions, e.g. asthma
- fever, high temperature
- following a heavy meal
- anaemia
- inflammation
- take care during pregnancy – with GP approval
- take care with the elderly – with GP approval.

Safety in exercise

This is essential and should come before any activity and relates to pre-screening your client before allowing them to take part. A simple questionnaire will help to identify any contra-indications and conditions requiring special care (see the above list).

The old idea of 'go for the burn' is obsolete and the emphasis is for a gentle approach, gradually warming up the body tissues and muscles. Environmental factors should be taken into account: if the floor to be used for exercising is not made of shock absorbing material, lower leg injury may occur. Good footwear is vital: exercise shoes should be well cushioned and provide stability to the lower leg and back. Consider the ventilation in the room: if the room is too warm it can lead to heat exhaustion.

Ensure that you have a bottle of water to hand and encourage your client to sip it regularly. Avoid potentially dangerous exercises and ensure that there is adequate space to allow freedom of movement.

TIP: If the room is not air-conditioned ensure that you have adequate natural ventilation by means of fans etc.

Fitness testing

This gives you, the therapist, an indication of your client's condition of health and fitness. It will also motivate your client if they are able to measure their fitness during a course of exercise and treatments, proving to them that their hard work is paying off.

Pre-Exercise Questionnaire

Please take 3 minutes to answer the following questions.
Just place a "✓" to indicate "Yes or Not Sure".

Name:.. Age:........................... Sex:...........................

Address:.. Post Code:...........................

Occupation:... Phone (work):........................... (home):...........................

Person to be contacted in case of accident:........................... Phone (work):........................... (home):...........................

Have you ever had or do you have?

If you ticked "✓"
Yes or Not sure

Anyone in your family under 60 suffered heart disease, stroke, raised cholesterol or sudden death? ☐ ☞

Are you male over 35 or female over 45 and NOT used to regular vigorous exercise? ☐ ☞

Are you on any prescribed medication? ☐   Have you been hospitalised recently? ☐ ☞

Have you given birth within the last 6 weeks? ☐   Are you pregnant? ☐ ☞

Do you have any infections or infectious diseases? ☐ ☞ ☞

Please take this form to your doctor and ask for clearance to exercise before starting any exercise programme

OR

sign below if you have already cleared the above condition with your doctor.

Do you have or have you had:

Gout ☐	Glandular Fever ☐	Any Heart Condition ☐ ☞	
Stroke ☐	Rheumatic Fever ☐	Heart murmur ☐ ☞	
Diabetes ☐	Dizziness or fainting ☐	High blood pressure >140/90 ☐ ☞	
Epilepsy ☐	Stomach or duodenal ulcer ☐	Palpitations or pains in the chest ☐ ☞	
Hernia ☐	Liver or kidney condition ☐	Raised cholesterol/Triglycerides ☐ ☞	

If you ticked please give details of conditions, medications and approximate date cleared

....

....

Condition cleared.

X...........................
Signed

Have you ever had or do you have?

If you ticked "✓"

Arthritis ☐	Any pain or major injuries particularly the following areas:			
Asthma ☐	Neck ☐	Back ☐	☞	
Cramps ☐	Knees ☐	Ankles ☐	☞	
Muscular pain ☐			☞	
Do you smoke? ☐	Are you dieting or fasting? ☐		☞	

Please ask instructor for exercise class or programme guidance before starting.

Are there any other conditions which may be reason to modify your exercise programme? ☐ ☞

What exercise have you been doing recently?

Exercise type:........................... Intensity (circle): Hard Medium Light   How long:........................... How often:...........................

Please read the following exercise advice carefully.

Ask any staff member to guide you into the most suitable class or programme. Work at a lower level on your first visit and concentrate on learning to do the exercises properly. On each visit you will be able to work a little harder. Be sure to limit yourself to a pace where you can still talk comfortably.

Should you suffer any injury, illness or condition in the future, please tell us by completing this form again.

It is recommended that all males over 35 and females over 45 should have a medical assessment including an exercise ECG and Cholesterol/Lipid count.

Statement

I recognise that the instructor is not able to provide me with medical advice with regard to my medical fitness and that this information is used as a guideline to the limitations of my ability to exercise. I have answered the questions to the best of my ability and understand the advice above.

Signed:... Date:...........................

Staff: Class/Programme: Time: Instructor:

Figure 6.12 Pre-exercise questionnaire

The uses of fitness testing

| motivation

| create an interest and awareness

| monitor improvement

| provide the exercise instructor with a base line from which they can plan.

Heart rate test

TIP: Advise your client not to smoke, eat or drink for at least two hours prior to this test.

1. Take your client's pulse – seated.

2. Instruct your client to exercise for two minutes: jogging, step-ups, skipping, cycling. Sit your client down and count the pulse again for six seconds.

TIP: After a few months of exercising the pulse rate (heart rate) will return more rapidly.

3. With your client in a seated position, take the pulse for six seconds at regular intervals until it returns to the resting level. Note the time taken for the pulse rate to drop.

4. Use the table to find your client's target heart rate: look for their age and follow the matrix line. This indicates the level of exercise intensity, helping you to appreciate a safe training range.

TIP: At rest an average male adult breathes in and out 16–18 times a minute. These values are 25 per cent lower in women.

Age	55%	60%	70%	80%	85%
15	19	21	24	27	29
20	18	20	23	27	28
25	18	19	23	26	28
30	17	19	22	25	27
35	17	19	22	25	26
40	17	18	21	24	26
45	16	18	20	23	25
50	16	17	20	23	24
55	15	17	19	22	23
60	15	16	19	21	23
65	14	16	18	21	22
70	14	15	18	20	21
75	13	15	17	19	21
80	13	14	16	19	20

Figure 6.13 Heart rate test

Strength tests

1. Upper arm and shoulder – hold you client's arm in the palms of both hands and resist the movements of flexion, extension and abduction, adduction and rotation.

2. Abdominal strength – ask your client if they are able to sit up from a lying position without assistance. If they can do this exercise without any difficulty ask them to repeat it more slowly.

TIP: Shaking of a muscle indicates fatigue.

Refer to flexibility tests on page 100.

The effects of exercise

- increased heart rate
- increased stroke volume – amount of blood pumped out with each heartbeat
- increased carbon dioxide output
- blood pressure increases initially but then regulates
- blood vessels expand in the working muscles
- blood vessels constrict in the areas not requiring blood – this is called blood 'shunting', hence blood travels in expanded vessels to respond to the demand in muscles working harder
- breathing becomes deeper and faster
- body temperature rises
- perspiration.

Warming up

It is vital to warm up before any form of physical activity in order to reduce the risk of injury and to maximise performance. During the warm up component the following will happen:

- body temperature, in particular muscle temperature will increase
- circulatory and respiratory systems are stimulated to meet the demands placed upon them
- synovial fluid is lubricated in the joints allowing more freedom of movement
- mentally prepares the exerciser for the activity to come.

Your aims are to educate your client in movements that:

- increases heart rate
- mobilise joints
- stretch main muscle groups – static 6–8 seconds.

Examples of warming up exercises:

- shoulder shrugging
- shoulder circling
- side stepping
- biceps curls
- hamstring curls
- knee bending
- trunk bending – into one side and then to the other
- heel/toe digging.

TIP: Avoid bouncy (ballistic) movements that cause muscle tightening brought about by a natural protective reflex action.

TIP: Introduce stretching only after you have mobilised and increased your client's pulse rate.

TIP: Avoid complicated movements; your aim is to motivate your client and it is vital they complete these exercises.

Figure 6.14 Quad stretch 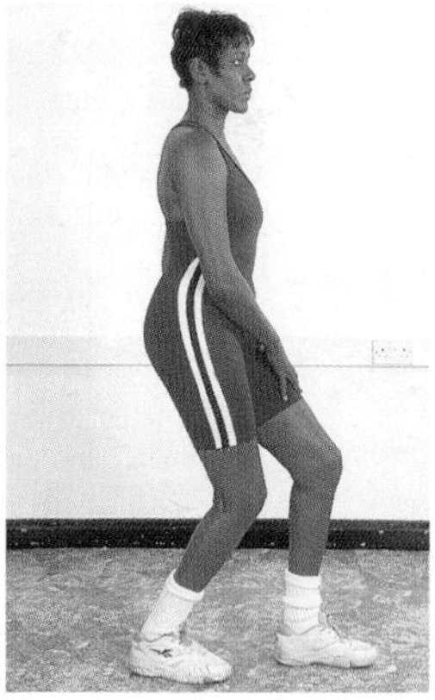   Figure 6.15 Calf stretch

Examples of preparatory stretches that can be used in a warm up are:

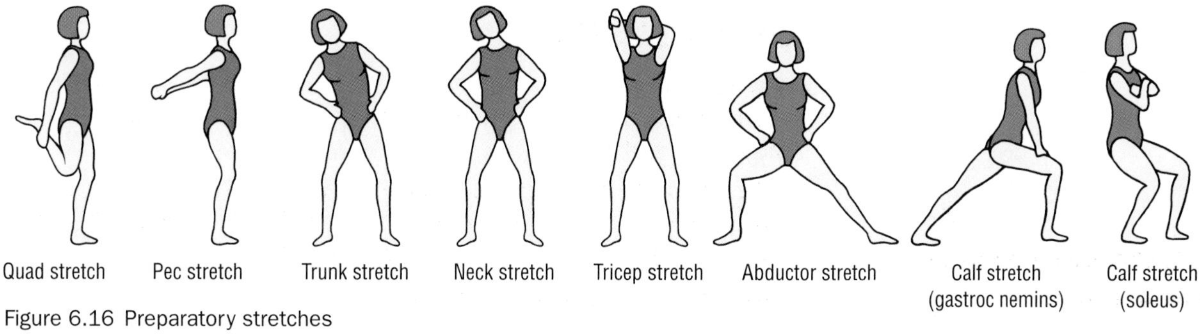

Quad stretch   Pec stretch   Trunk stretch   Neck stretch   Tricep stretch   Abductor stretch   Calf stretch (gastroc nemins)   Calf stretch (soleus)

Figure 6.16 Preparatory stretches

Cooling down/relaxation

These exercises enable the body to cool down slowly and the breathing to return to normal.

Progression and adaptation

To apply the concept of progression we use the 4 Rs. The 4 Rs are:

l resistance

l repetitions

l rest

l rate.

> **TIP: Progressing and adapting exercise keeps your client motivated.**

To progress with exercise adapt the level of stress or force so that it imposes a demand on the body systems; that is, make the exercise harder by adapting one of the 4 Rs. Adaptation is required to provide an alternative exercise for the individual as ability will vary.

Note: refer to the sample exercise plan.

Exercise Description Isotonic/Isometric	Sets & Rep's	Objective	Muscle Group	Teaching Points	Progression and Adaptation
Sit up	4 x ⅛	To tone and strengthen the abdomen	rectus abdominus	lower back to floor • breathe out as you raise • bend legs feet flat to floor • control movement • abdomen pulled in • Do not jerk the neck	P – lengthen leverage or increase exercise sets, slow down A. take arms across the chest in to tomb position

Figure 6.17 An exercise plan

> **TIP: When teaching older clients ensure that you utilise the props at hand, e.g. chair, table, etc.**

Figure 6.18 A correct sit-up

Types of muscle contraction

Isotonic exercise can be defined as where the muscle changes in length and results in joint movement. These movements may be:

l concentric (shortening of the muscle). An example of a concentric movement is the upward phase of a push up or biceps curl.

l eccentric (lengthening of the muscle). An example of an eccentric movement is the downward phase of a push up or biceps curl.

l isometric (static). These movements do not involve the muscle changing in length, there is no joint movement but there is an increase in muscle tone.

Figure 6.19 Concentric – works against the direction of gravity

Figure 6.20 Eccentric – works in the direction of gravity

TIP: Knowledge of the types of muscle contracting is important when adapting exercises to suit your client's individual ability.

Useful terms

Passive movement – no muscle work is carried out by your client but may be carried out by you the therapist or a machine.

Active movement – these may be assisted in that an external force is applied, if muscle strength is inadequate.

Free – these movements use your client's own efforts, developing tone, co-ordination, mobility and relaxation.

Resisted movement – an external force is applied opposing the force of the muscle contraction. This may be in the form of springs, water weights, therapist or client.

Prime movers of Agonists – these muscles are those that contract to produce the movement.

Antagonist – these are the opposite group to the prime movers; they relax and lengthen as the prime mover contracts.

Synergist – these are the muscles that help the prime mover to perform an efficient movement.

Fixators – these muscles enable the movement to take place from a fixed base, stabilising the joint.

Figure 6.21 Correct knee alignment

Flexibility

This term refers to the possible range of movement of a joint or group of joints. Regular stretching improves the capacity to extend fully and allows the joint a free range of movement. Regular stretching:

- improves co-ordination between muscle groups
- prevents injury
- improves relaxation of muscles
- reduces the risk of muscles tightening
- increases extendibility of muscle.

TIP: The more active the person is the more flexible they are likely to be.

TIP: Stiffness is often associated with age as elasticity is lost, resulting in stiffer tighter muscles.

Figure 6.22 Abductor stretch

Figure 6.23 Spine stretch, lower back and hamstrings

Figure 6.24 Gluteal stretch

TIP: A person is more flexible when the body tissues are warm.

TIP: The quadriceps muscles play an important role in pelvic alignment.

TIP: Advise your client to breathe slowly and evenly while stretching. Do not overstretch to the point of pain. Avoid ballistic stretching (bouncing).

Flexibility tests

Sit and reach

This test makes an assessment of the suppleness in the lower back and hamstrings, which are common sites for tightness. Ask the client to:

- sit on the floor, long sitting position
- place the soles of the feet against a flat surface
- bend forward reaching to touch the toes and past them, if your client can.

If your client cannot touch their toes it is a poor result, touching their toes it is an average result and reaching beyond their toes is good.

Hamstring test

- the client lies on their back facing the ceiling
- raises one leg vertically
- the therapist may stabilise the raised leg.

If the result is less that 90 degrees at hip the result is poor, 90 degrees is average and 105 degrees is good.

Quadriceps test

- the client lies on their stomach, face down, with their legs straight
- bend knee, heel towards the buttocks
- the therapist may stabilise the heel.

If the heel cannot touch the buttock the result is poor. The heel touching the buttocks is average and the heel touching the buttocks, without resistance, is very good.

Controversial exercises

Double leg lifting

Figure 6.25 Double leg lifting

During this dangerous exercise the client lies on the ground and lifts both legs, keeping them straight and moving them to a vertical position from the hips. Although this exercise was initially thought to be good for strengthening the abdominals, it is really working the flexors of the hips.

The muscles are not simply working against the weight of the leg, but the weight of the leg multiplied by the length of the leg and are also working at a great disadvantage. The lower back comes to the floor and the abdominal wall, therefore they are distended forwards and strained and may tremble. The exerciser may hold their breath in an attempt to stabilise the movement. The circular part of the pelvic floor muscle around the urethra, being unable to withstand the increasing pressure in the abdominal cavity, may bring about a slight gush of urine (which often the performer is too embarrassed to mention).

Note: please refer to the sample exercise plan, where the correct technique for working the abdominals is explained.

Other exercises to be avoided

Exercise	Reason	Alternatives
Neck rotation	Excessive hypertension	Controlled liner movements
Straight leg sit ups	Damages lower back due to pressure inflicted on discs between vertebrae	Bend leg into a flexed position
Hyperextension of back	May put unnecessary pressure on the lower back	Raise one arm and opposing leg separately
Forced hyperextension	Intervertebral compression, ligament strain	Lie on the stomach, pull elbows in close, raise slowly as far as is comfortable
High leg extensions on all fours	Hyperextends the back	A controlled movement on elbows is more stable. Keep back flat
Rapid toe touching	Ballistic lower back damage	Sit and reach
Deep squats	Ligament damage. Patella may be injured	Half squats
Hurdles, stretch with bent leg turned away from the body	Ligaments twisted uncomfortably	Tuck bent leg under bottom or around the front
Long arm circles (through a small range of movement)	Potentially dangerous to shoulder tendons	Large range of movement
Jumping too fast, straight knees	Causes shin splints	Slow speed down, bring heel to the floor
Legs over head stretch	Over stresses the neck	Seated upper back stretcher. Sit cross legged and bend back forwards

Exercise for over 50s

There are certain factors to be considered when working with the over 50s, but provided that care is taken in the progression at the exercise plan, working out can be very beneficial. Factors to consider:

- take more time to warm up
- range of movement may be limited particularly in the back, neck and shoulders, therefore take extra care, gradually increasing repetitions
- abdominal and back muscles may be weak and require strengthening.

Exercising in pregnancy and post natal exercise

As a general rule there is no reason why a healthy pregnant woman, who normally exercises, should not continue with their GP's consent. It is vital that you educate your client to understand the changes taking place in their body and their relationship to exercise.

Posture will differ in pregnancy, as the baby throws body weight forwards, the lumbar curve increases, as does the pelvic tilt. This puts great strain on the lumber spine. Posture awareness and correction is an important aspect of anti-natal exercise.

Figure 6.26 Extension

SUMMARY

You will have found from reading this chapter, that the aspects of client fitness are very broad and as a beauty therapist you will need to have a focus on all aspects. There are a number of contra indications to exercise and care must be taken to provide sound advice. Home care exercises may be given to support your client's course of salon treatment however, you must be realistic in the setting of goals. The success of treatment will be the result of thorough consultation and exercises pitched for the individual.

Your treatment programme will be more effective if you evaluate and review your client's progress at regular intervals, giving you the opportunity to progress and adapt as the client responds to treatment.

Finally, if you are in any doubt about the suitability of your client to undertake this type of regime, obtain their doctor's approval.

FURTHER STUDY

1. Find out about the terms:

    a) cellulite

    b) vegan

    c) metabolic rate

    d) blood pressure.

2. Prepare a beginner level warm up for a 20–25 year old with no contra-indications.

3. Research the mechanisms of respiration.

4. To assist you in providing your clients with good advice, research the issues of dietary fads and dietary aids. Look at several types of diet and discuss their advantages and disadvantages. You may wish to consider:

    ❙ appetite suppressers

    ❙ low fat diets

    ❙ fruit diets

    ❙ high fibre diets

    ❙ Hay diets

    ❙ commercial dietary products.

5. Describe the correct tilt of the pelvis and draw diagrams to represent the following posture faults:

    a) anterior pelvic tilt

    b) posterior pelvic tilt

    c) lateral pelvic tilt.

6. Design 6 homecare exercises for a middle aged client, who is generally unfit and has booked a course of electrical muscular stimulation and G5. She has slack muscle tone on her abdomen, inner thighs and buttocks.

7. Plan a 1 hour relaxation session to include treatments and exercise for an elderly client.

8. Give one reason why your client should wear disposable or washable foot wear when walking from the shower to the treatment area.

Review questions

1. Name one source of fat in a diet.

2. How does the human body digest carbohydrate?

3. How much water would you advise your client to drink each day?

4. Describe how you could adapt a full press-up.

5. Summarise why 'double leg lifting' is a dangerous exercise.

6. Ask your client to make a note on her eating habits and discuss them during her next treatment at the salon.

7. What is meant by good muscle tone and how would you recognise it?

8. Give reasons why flexibility is an important component of fitness.

Body massage

This chapter introduces you to the application of body massage techniques. You will be provided with step by step instruction of the classical movements, the selection and use of massage medium available and the care of your client.

It is vital that you are able to identify contra indications and contra actions to treatment in order that you carry out safe working practice in the salon.

Elements

15.1 Assess clients for body massage

15.2 Prepare the treatment room and client for body massage

15.3 Massage the body to meet client requirements

CONTENTS

Preparation   105

Main massage movements   106

Massage routine   108

Completion of treatment   112

Summary   113

Further Study   113

Review questions   113

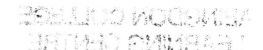

BODY MASSAGE

Massage is the manipulation of the soft tissues of the body. Each manipulation produces its own effects locally on the area being treated and generally on the whole body. Everyone can benefit from the stress-reducing effects of massage, that may help to relieve a variety of problems including postural disorders, physiological illness and general muscular aches and pains.

Preparation

The massage service should be provided in a tranquil environment; this will help to relax your client and put them at ease. At their first treatment, it is likely that they will feel a little nervous and uncertain of what to expect. To reduce such uncertainty always explain the treatment process, in understandable terms, before providing the treatment to your client. Maintain a polite and respectful manner when dealing with your client.

Pre-massage treatments may include any of the following: paraffin wax, infra-red, audio sound and heat inducing products.

Your treatment room should be organised well in advance of your client's arrival. The couch should be prepared with clean towels and disposable coverings. Your client will need to be covered with clean, warm towels, which also serve to protect their modesty. Your client's hair should be protected off their face and shoulders.

The following items should be located on the treatment trolley:

l massage medium – oil, cream, talc (oil is the most frequently used medium but an alternative may be used in the case of oil allergy; specific creams may be used in the treatment of cellulite)

l clean cotton wool

l antiseptic

l eau de cologne

l headband

l disposable tissue

l record card.

All essentials should be located on the treatment trolley before the treatment commences. Continuity can be lost if the treatment is interrupted as the therapist searches for products or equipment. Take extra care with elderly clients; they may require a helping hand on and off the treatment couch. Have plenty of supporting cushions at the ready and a chair nearby for them to sit on when removing clothes, shoes, etc.

Before commencing with the treatment check your client for contra-indications. Should you discover any contra-indications explain the implications of these and the action to be taken in a sensitive and unemotional manner. Contra-indications include:

l abnormal blood pressure

l thrombosis/embolism/phlebitis

l epilepsy

l skin disorders/infections, e.g. Acne, Ringworm, impetigo, cold sores, etc.

l extensive bruising/muscular swelling/inflammation

l recent haemorrhage/recent scar tissue/recent operations (obtain GP's written consent)

TIP: It is extremely important to concentrate on your client when performing a body massage. If you are anxious, stressed or irritable, you could transmit these emotions to your client.

TIP: To create the perfect atmosphere why not burn some relaxing aromatherapy oils, play relaxation music (a licence may be required), have a selection of herbal pillows in the room, dim the lights and ensure that the room is both warm and well ventilated.

TIP: Have pillows available, for support, should your client need them. A rolled-up towel may be used when pillows are not available.

TIP: Mineral oil should be avoided for body massage as research suggests that it blocks the skin's pores.

TIP: There are a range of ready to use blended oils on the market these are only recommended for use by qualified aromatherapists.

ABINGDON COLLEGE
LEARNING CENTRE

TIP: If you are in any doubt about your client's condition, seek their GP's advice. Some of the mentioned contra-indications may be treated with the consent of the client's GP.

TIP: You are working closely with your client therefore personal hygiene must be faultless – take care of personal breath and body freshness.

- warts or moles
- recent fractures/sprains
- metal placements
- electronic implants
- heart defects
- respiratory disease
- fever/feeling unwell
- Hepatitis or HIV
- currently under medical care
- loss of tactile sensation
- abdominal area during pregnancy or the first few days of menstruation
- cuts or abrasions
- varicose veins/heeled varicose ulcers.

It is vital that you are not disturbed when carrying out a massage treatment. Somebody entering the cubicle or making a noise would not only disturb your client's relaxation but also invade their privacy. Treatment timing varies according to the area of the body being treated; for example, a back massage will take approximately 30 minutes and a full body massage 60 minutes.

Massage movements

There are five main types of massage movements, each having its own specific effects, uses and contra-indications.

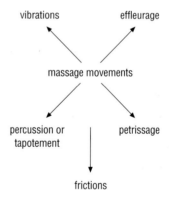

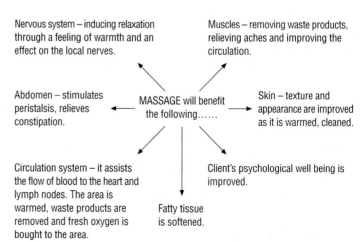

Effleurage

This is a firm stroking-style movement and is used at the beginning of a routine to accustom your client to your touch. It also aids the distribution of the massage oil/cream. It can be used as a linking movement between areas and other movements and is also used to wind down the massage routine at the end. This movement is the most widely used in the routine. Your hand is moulded to the body part being treated and following the direction of the blood flow. Your hand should glide over the area, with an even rhythm, finishing at the nearest lymphatic node. Pressure must be even and firm in the upward phase of the movement, taking blood to the heart.

Effects

- creates erythema (redness, increases capillary blood flow) and therefore stimulates the circulation
- hastens the removal of waste products from metabolism through stimulation of lymphatic flow
- soothes and induces relaxation
- stimulates glandular activity
- mobilises soft tissue.

Effleurage may cause discomfort if performed over very hirsute (hairy) areas.

Stroking is a movement similar to effleurage but its pressure is much lighter and can be performed in any direction; a sedative effect is produced when performed slowly and a stimulating effect when performed quickly.

Petrissage

This deep kneading movement is typically carried out over a group of muscles or an individual one. It may be done with one hand or reinforced with the free hand on top of the working one for deeper penetration. It can be performed on small areas, using the pads of the fingers or thumbs. This compression manipulation is applied, with pressure, in the upward phase of the movement. The effects of circular kneading:

- stimulates circulation
- eliminates waste products
- warms the tissues
- draws nutrients to the area
- improves the skin's functions and condition
- soothes nerve endings
- mobilises subcutaneous tissue
- stimulates penstalsis.

Petrissage has several modifications in addition to circular kneading which are: picking up, wringing and skin rolling.

Picking up

This manipulates a specific muscle or muscle group which are being grasped, picked up, squeezed and relaxed with one or both hands, or thumb and fingers. The effects of picking up:

- stimulates
- loosens fibrous adhesions.

Wringing

This stretching and twisting movement requires both hands over the muscle and tissue. The effects of wringing are:

I shortened structures may be stretched.

Skin rolling

Another stretching manipulation performed with both hands, fingers on one side and thumbs on the others. The subcutaneous tissues are moved on the muscles and bones. The effects of skin rolling:

I loosens tight subcutaneous tissue

I produces redness

I loosens adhesions

I improves skin tissue

I softens the site of scar tissue.

Note: Skin rolling and wringing should not be performed on stretched skin or poorly toned skin.

Frictions

Small deep movements performed using circular or transverse directions with the middle or index finger. The effects of frictions:

I loosens and stretches thickenings that may have resulted from inflammation

I creates redness, softens and aids removal of waste products from the area.

Percussion or tapotement

A stimulating movement that has several modifications: hacking, cupping or heavy percussions.

I Hacking – a light and rapid movement striking the skin with the backs of the third, fourth and fifth fingers.

I Cupping – with hands slightly cupped, alternately contacting the skin with the palm of the hand.

I Heavy percussion – movements involve pounding and beating using the side or front of a fist over well covered areas like the gluteals. The effects of heavy percussion increase circulation. This movement should never be performed over client's weak muscles or extensively bruised areas.

Vibrations

A light, trembling movement performed by placing the flat of the palms on the body part and vibrating the forearm. The effects of vibration may be soothing over the path of a nerve.

Massage routine

Ensure that your client is kept warm with modesty towels at all times. Stand in a 'walk standing' position with your front leg bent. You will be able to massage the whole of the length of the leg without taking a step by just transferring your body weight as you move up the limb. If you need to move around the room, do so quietly and calmly so as not to disturb your client's relaxation. When your client is comfortable on the couch, wipe both their feet with antiseptic.

TIP: Protect your client's modesty at all times by providing adequate time to undress and make them feel comfortable.

Figure 7.1 Positioning of client prior to manual massage

The body massage has a routine order or areas of the body to be treated. For the technique described in this book the orders is:

1. front of leg (right)
   a. top of leg
   b. knee and lower leg
2. arm (right)
3. front of leg (left)
   a. top of leg
   b. knee and lower leg,
4. arm (left)
5. abdomen
6. chest
7. back massage
   a whole back
   b. upper back
   c. lower back
8. back of leg (right)
   a whole leg
   b. top of leg and buttocks
   c. lower leg
9. back of leg (left)
   a. whole leg
   b. top of leg and buttocks
   c. lower leg.

1. Front of leg massage (start on client's right side)

Place a rolled towel under the knee for support.

1. Effleurage to the outside of the leg from ankle to thigh and return, stroking down the inside of the leg to the ankle. Repeat 8 times.

a. Top of leg

2. Effleurage up to the top of the leg and perform single-handed kneading to the thigh between hip and knee, supporting the limb with your free hand. Repeat 8 times, swap hands and repeat.

3. Repeat this movement by alternate-handed kneading to area and repeat 8 times.

4. Pick up and squeeze (petrissage) to the whole upper leg.

TIP: Your client may feel cold from time to time so don't forget to ask her if they are warm and comfortable and always have spare towels at hand.

TIP: If you are using massage cream, to reduce the risk of cross infection this should be removed from the tub using a clean spatula.

5. If the area is well covered (plentiful subcutaneous tissue), hacking, cupping and pounding to the outside of thigh only. (This can be carried out over a towel if necessary.)

6. Effleurage the top of the leg. Repeat 8 times.

Cover the top of the leg.

b. Knee and lower leg

7. Double thumb kneading around the knee joint, placing your supporting fingers around the back of the knee joint.

8. Manipulate the knee cap, gently moving it from side to side and up and down (check that your client has no medical problems in this area as this may contra-indicate).

9. Effleurage the calf from the ankle to the knee. Repeat 8 times.

10. Single handed kneading to the calf muscle.

11. Basic foot massage (to be adopted from your pedicure routine).

12. Repeat movement no. 1 (front of leg).

Now remove the supporting towel from under your client's knee.

2. Arm massage (right)

Uncover one arm and offer support if required.

1. Hold the arm in the 'hand shaking' position, effleurage up to the shoulder and down with your left hand. Turn your client's palm upwards and effleurage with your right hand up to the axilla and down. Repeat 8 times.

2. Petrissage (single handed) to the top of the arm, working from shoulder to elbow with the left hand, support limb with your free hand. Repeat with right hand to the inside of the upper arm.

3. 'Pick up and squeeze' (petrissage) the deltoid muscle. Support the limb with the freehand.

4. Fold your client's arm over their chest and pick up and squeeze the triceps muscles.

5. Cupping and light hacking may also be carried out, provided that the area is well covered.

6. Single-handed petrissage to the front of the forearm, from the elbow to the hand. Repeat 8 times.

7. Double thumb kneading to forearm from the wrist to the elbow, first to the front and then to the back of the limb.

8. Hand massage (adapt your manicure routine).

9. Finish with movement no. 1.
   Cover the arm and remove any supporting pillows.

3. Front of leg massage/4. Arm massage(left)

Now repeat the leg and arm massage to your client's left side, move to the left side of your client and couch. When completed walk back around to your client's right side. Uncover the abdomen taking great care to protect your client's modesty.

5. Abdomen massage

1. Effleurage from the hips, up the side of the trunk and stroke down the centre of the abdomen over the ribs towards the pubis. Repeat 8 times.

2. Double-handed and single-handed petrissage 8 times (5 circles). Work down the back of the trunk to the hips and over the abdomen.

❛TIP: Ensure that your client is warm and neatly covered throughout. ❜

❛TIP: The use of eau de cologne is very refreshing and serves as a useful medium to remove the excess oil. ❜

❛TIP: Use a bath sheet (towel) to cover your client's legs and tuck a disposable towel in the brief line to protect their underwear. ❜

3. 'Pick up and squeeze' the sides of the body, petrissage from one side to the other.

4. Skin rolling on the ribs (working from the mid-line of the body outwards).

5. Stroke across the abdomen with alternate hands.

6. Repeat the effleurage as in no. 1. Repeat 8 times.
Cover the abdomen and uncover the chest.

6. Chest massage

1. Effleurage over the shoulder and up the nape of the neck and then down across the chest 8 times.

2. Reinforced effleurage (the added pressure applied by the second hand on top of the first), making a figure movement over the shoulders, alternately.

3. 'Pick up and squeeze' on the upper fibres of the trapezius muscle, working from the neck outwards to the shoulder. First on one side and then the other.

4. Both hands – petrissage the shoulders. Repeat 8 times.

5. Six sweeping petrissage circles across the chest, effleurage back to the shoulder using both hands from left to right.

6. 'Pick up and squeeze' on deltoids, first on one side and then the other.

7. Wringing and skin rolling, if the area is well covered.

8. Repeat the effleurage as in no. 1. Repeat 8 times.

Turn your client over, hold the side of the towel nearest to you and ask the client to turn towards you. Ensure that your client is warm and comfortable. It may be necessary to remove any head support used earlier.

7. Back massage
Expose the back and tuck a disposable tissue in the brief line to protect your client's clothes.

a. Whole back

1. Effleurage from the base of the spine up the centre back, across the shoulder and down the side of the body to the hip. Repeat 8 times.

2. Petrissage with both hands together as many circles as possible. Repeat 8 times, all the way from the shoulder down to the hips.

With a small towel cover your client's lower back.

b. Concentrate on the upper back.

3. Nape of the neck – effleurage up the nape of the neck to the hair line and then thumb kneading down.

4. Wringing on trapezius from the neck to the shoulder and then back.

5. Thumb kneading at the base of the neck and then gradually larger circles to the shoulder.

6. Wringing on the upper back.

7. Petrissage around the scapula (thumb, finger or whole hand).

Cover the top of the back and shoulders to keep the area warm

c. Concentrate on the lower back

8. Effleurage, petrissage and reinforced petrissage on the lower back.

TIP: When moving to the lower back, use a spare towel to keep the upper back warm.

9. 'Pick up and squeeze' the sides of the trunk.

10. Wringing over all the lower back.

11. Skin rolling over the ribs.

12. Hacking (in the direction of the ribs) and cupping, if your client requires it.

d. Relaxation

13. Knuckling up the spine to the nape of the neck.

14. Stroking to the whole of the back.

15. Vibrations.

16. Repeat effleurage, as for no. 1. Repeat 8 times.

17. Frictions – slowly down the spine.

18. Vibrations (down the length of the spine, alternate the hands).

19. Stroking, longitudinal or horizontally.

20. Repeat effleurage, as for no. 1. Repeat 8 times.

21. On the last effleurage, put pressure on the hips and then gently release.

8. Back of leg massage (right)/8. Back of leg massage (left)

Place a rolled towel under the front of the foot for support.

a. Whole leg

1. Single-handed effleurage from ankle to gluteals and back.

b. Top of leg and buttocks

2. Single-handed kneading from the buttock to the knee. Repeat 8 times. Follow this with double-handed and alternate-handed kneading. Repeat this on the inside of the thigh.

3. 'Pick up and squeeze' the inside of the thigh.

4. Hacking, cupping, beating, pounding on gluteds and thigh, if not contra-indicated.

5. Effleurage to the top of the leg. Repeat 8 times.

Cover the top of the leg.

c. Lower leg (knee to ankle)

6. Effleurage the calf, knee to ankle. Repeat 8 times.

7. Knead the calf from knee to ankle, first with one hand and then the other.

8. 'Pick up and squeeze' to the calf.

9. Hacking and cupping on the calf, from the knee to ankle.

10. Finish with effleurage to the whole leg, as in no. 1. Repeat 8 times.

Completion of treatment

Remove the towel support and place under the opposite foot and now repeat to the other leg.

Excess oil or cream remaining on the skin may be removed using a cotton wool pad moistened with eau de cologne. Some clients prefer to leave residual oils on the skin.

Turn your client over, help them with robe, assist them when sitting up and putting feet down on the floor as they may feel a little dizzy.

TIP: Don't forget to remind your client to put their jewellery back on following completion of the treatment.

TIP: Some couches have a breathing hole to ensure client comfort during back massage. This enables clients to breath freely and to keep their spine straight. Rolling a towel and placing it between the forehead and couch provides extra comfort.

TIP: On completion of treatment allow five minutes for your client to rest before getting dressed.

Clean up all materials, equipment and working area ready for your next treatment.

Wash your hands and give your client homecare advice, this should include a period of rest when they return home. Don't forget to recommend any products that would assist the effectiveness of your treatment objectives.

SUMMARY

Although body massage is one of the most enjoyable treatments to receive, you should be aware that it is a physically demanding treatment to give. Therefore your salon receptionist will need to allocate a short 'rest period' between bookings if you have consecutive massage treatments in your column, this will enable you to give an effective and competent treatment for each client.

The essentials of a Swedish body massage are outlined in this chapter but it must be noted that you will learn to adapt your techniques for every client and their individual needs. For example, a male client would not require abdominal massage but may need more attention given to his back.

Finally, the most effect treatment may be given when you ensure a welcoming and professional environment. This may include the temperature of the room, some suitable music and the burning of essential oils which aim to provide a relaxing atmosphere.

FURTHER STUDY

1. Read this chapter and discuss the types of pre-massage treatments your salon could offer and how they could be incorporated into a body massage treatment.

2. Explain how you could adapt your techniques to achieve relaxation on a stressed client.

3. Identify why each of the following may restrict treatment:- menstruation, pregnancy, a bruised knee and a slim client.

4. List the systemic medical conditions that may contra-indicate treatment.

5. Obtain a price list from two salons and compare the cost and duration of massage treatment.

6. Describe where you might include hacking within your routine.

Review Questions

1. List the homecare and aftercare advice you would give your client following a massage treatment.

2. What action would you take if your client suffered an allergic reaction?

3. Describe the appearance of erythema.

4. It is advisable to not only be hygienic but to be seen to be hygienic. Explain this statement.

5. What extra precautions should you take when dealing with an elderly client?

Body treatments

This chapter introduces you to mechanical and electrical treatments for the body and should be used in conjunction with the figure analysis chapter. As a Beauty Therapist, you will be expected to assess your client and through expert consultation technique, discuss your recommendations with them. The correct selection and application of body treatments will improve your client's body condition.

Unit 14

14.1 Assess clients and prepare treatment plans

14.2 Prepare the treatment room and client for mechanical and electrical treatments

14.3 Treat clients using mechanical and electrical equipment

CONTENTS

Consultation	115
Sensitivity tests	115
Gyratory Vibrator	116
Audio sound	118
Percussion	118
Vacuum Suction	119
Galvanic	121
Faradic Type treatment (neuro-muscular electrical treatment)	122
Summary	126
Further Questions	126
Review Questions	127

PRELIMINARY CONSULTATION

Chapter 6 should be used in conjunction with this chapter as it will enable you to recommend the most suitable course of treatment for your client and offer effective homecare advice.

Your assessment technique should identify your client's medical history, contraindications, emotional and physical condition. It is vital that you ask questions about her lifestyle as adaptations may need to be made and it will give you an idea of how flexible they will be regarding the frequency and duration of their visits to you.

Remember, that a consultation is a two way process, you should give your client the opportunity to ask any questions and to voice the expectations of their treatment. If you do identify any contraindications or are in any doubt whether to go ahead with treatment, you must tactfully refer them to their G.P. for approval. You will also be required to use your observational skills and body analysis before a treatment can be recommended and this may take an additional 30 minutes.

You must explain the treatments in detail, outlining cost involved, duration and sensation of each treatment.

When the record card is complete you should ask your client to sign and agree.

An appropriate treatment plan may include:

I Medical history

I Known contra-indications

I Known contra-actions

I Lifestyle pattern

I Emotional and physical condition

I Skin analysis

I Figure analysis

I Skin test results

I Areas requiring treatment

I Previous treatment history

I Type, duration and objectives of treatment

I Treatment details in date order

I Aftercare advice/purchases made

I Client signature

I Client feedback.

N.B. a second figure analysis card may be completed which addresses your client's posture, weight, height, measurements, % of body fat and any muscle tests carried out. The regular updating of these details, can serve to motivate your client as treatment progresses.

SKIN SENSITIVITY TESTS

There are two basic skin sensitivity tests that may be carried out before electrical treatment may be given.

'The sharp and soft test', uses a sharp instrument such as a cuticle stick and something soft such as cotton wool. Instruct your client to close their eyes and apply the items randomly to the surface of the area requiring treatment.

'The hot and cold test', uses two containers e.g. test tubes one filled with hot water and the other filled with cold water. This tests your client's sensitivity as randomly the tubes are applied to the area and your client is asked to identify the hot from the cold. If for any reason your client is unable to identify the sensations and you suspect their skin sensation is not intact, do not proceed with treatment.

Treatment may be given when your client agrees to the treatment plan and there are no contra indications.

Gyratory Vibrator

The gyratory vibrator gives one of the most popular of the mechanical treatments that may be given on it's own using the full range of massage heads, each representing a massage movement or together with manual massage.

Figure 8.1 A range of vibratory equipment

TIP: The massage heads are made of durable rubber or polyurethane and are attached to a drive cable (hose) that connects to the motor.

This type of massage will be heavier than a manual technique, therefore it is only indicated for the well-covered, larger areas.

The two main units used for vibratory massage are the popular floor standing unit or the smaller, compact, hand-held vibro mat that has fewer attachments but is ideal for the mobile practice.

TIP: First pre-heat the body tissues to achieve more effective results.

Effects

- stimulation of blood flow hence erythema
- increased cellular metabolism
- desquamation
- created warmth inducing relaxation
- relief of tension and elimination of waste products
- mobilisation of fatty deposits
- encouragement and motivation for clients to loose weight.

Application

1. Explain the treatment to your client whilst checking for contra-indications on the areas requiring treatment. Contra-indications include:
- loose creepy skin
- bony areas (lacking in subcutaneous fat)
- abdomenal swelling
- pregnancy
- menstruation

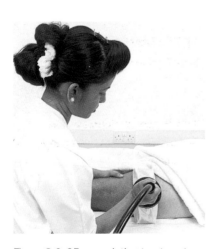

Figure 8.2 G5: completing treatment

- extremely hairy areas
- skin diseases and disorders
- diabetes – obtain GP approval prior to use
- epileptics – obtain GP approval prior to use
- bruising
- varicose veins, thrombosis or phlebitis
- oedema
- spinal problems
- skin tags, moles
- recent scar tissue
- vascular conditions.

2. Ensure that you have thoroughly cleansed and dried the treatment area then apply a liberal covering of talc.

3. Test the machine on yourself first, then thoroughly clean the attachment.

4. Using the selected attachments in an appropriate order, proceed with the treatment. Each attachment is used either in a rotary or stroking motion. Refer to manufacturer's guidelines.

5. When the desired effect has been achieved, move to the next area for treatment.

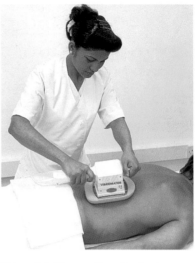

Figure 8.3 Vibro matt on the back

Figure 8.4 A selection of G5 applicators

TIP: Keep your client warm and covered with modesty towels throughout, exposing only the area to be treated.

TIP: As with all treatments, remove jewellery before commencing the treatment.

TIP: Keep heads clean by scrubbing in soapy water.

TIP: Too much pressure or prolonged treatment can cause bruising.

TIP: Audio sonic is not to be confused with ultra sound.

TIP: There are commonly two heads accompanying this unit – one flat and one ball-shaped.

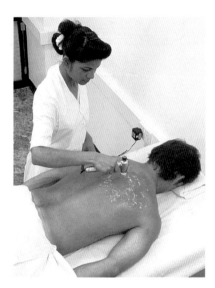

Figure 8.5 Application of audiosonic to the back

TIP: Avoid sensitive areas, e.g. the eyes and bony areas.

TIP: Care should be taken when treating the back of the neck as nausea may be experienced.

Audio sonic vibrator

This is an effective treatment in the removal of muscular tension, aches and pains, using a light-weight, hand-held unit. The attachment is selected and screwed into the sound wave vibrator. Unlike the gyratory massager the attachment does not rotate but simply sends vibrations accompanied by a humming noise deeply into the tissues, twanging the muscle fibres written their sheath.

Effects

- increase in blood flow, hence erythema
- warmth in the tissues induces relaxation
- stimulation of cellular metabolism
- desquamation
- restores elasticity to muscle tissue.

Application

1. Prepare the client by cleansing and drying the area and ensure that they are comfortable and informed of the treatment.
2. Check for contra-indications:
   - migraine sufferers (avoid head and neck)
   - bony areas around the eye and ear
   - areas lacking subcutaneous tissue
   - broken capillaries/vascular areas
   - skin disease
   - inflammation
   - skin tags or moles
   - open wounds.
3. Secure the selected head into the vibrator and test the machine on yourself, then clean the head. Apply to the skin, using rotary or back and forth movements. Use cream or purified talc as your selected medium.
4. Continue until the desired effect has been achieved.
5. Remove medium and complete the treatment. Clean the head with soapy water.

Percussion vibrator

This treatment requires a substantial amount of subcutaneous tissue as its vibrations resemble the tapotement movement of manual massage. When applied a rippling effect is achieved as the rotary movements are performed. This treatment may be used on the face, neck and shoulders.

Effects

- softens subcutaneous tissue
- creates an erythema
- desquamation
- warms and relaxes.

Application

The application is undertaken in a similar manner to the audio sound treatment.

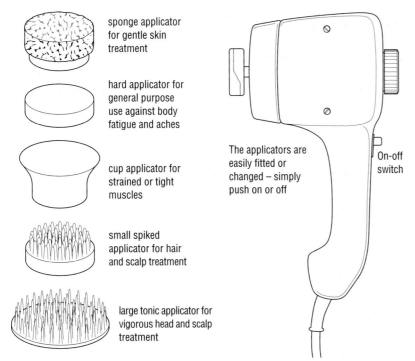

sponge applicator for gentle skin treatment

hard applicator for general purpose use against body fatigue and aches

cup applicator for strained or tight muscles

small spiked applicator for hair and scalp treatment

large tonic applicator for vigorous head and scalp treatment

The applicators are easily fitted or changed – simply push on or off

On-off switch

Figure 8.6 Hand percussion vibrator with applicator

TIP: You may apply this treatment indirectly over the area using your hand between the body part and the applicator. This will have a slight decreasing effect on the vibrations but can make the treatment more comfortable in some areas as well as being a suitable way of introducing the treatment to the slightly nervous client.

Vacuum Suction

This treatment aims to assist the movement of lymphatic fluid towards the main lymphatic nodes, resulting in elimination of waste products and toxins. It also stimulates the circulatory system and is used as part of a figure improvement programme in conjunction with other body treatments. This treatment must be given as a course in order to be effective and it is suggested that you recommend your client attends 2-3 times a week for 12 treatments.

Figure 8.7 Body cups

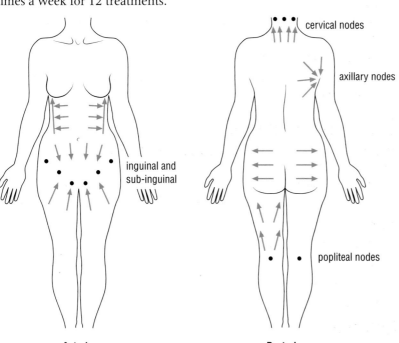

cervical nodes

axillary nodes

inguinal and sub-inguinal

popliteal nodes

Anterior

Posterior

Figure 8.8 Direction of strokes and main lymph nodes on the body

TIP: This treatment should, ideally, be packaged as a course of 10–12 treatments, with your client attending 2–3 times per week.

TIP: The body tissues are more receptive if pre-heated.

Effects

- A general improvement in the appearance of cellulite.
- Stimulation of both lymphatic and blood circulation.
- Spot reduction on specific areas such as thighs, buttocks and hips, when combined with diet and exercise.
- Desquamation (removal of dead skin cells)
- Reduction of non-systemic Odema and areas of fluid retention.
- Scar tissue may be softened.
- Stimulates cellular metabolism.

Application

1. Ensure your client is comfortable on the couch, remember that their modesty and privacy must be respected at all times. Inspect the area to be treated for contraindications:-
   - Diseases and disorders of the skin
   - Bruising
   - Broken skin
   - Breast tissue
   - Thread veins or varicose veins
   - Loose or crepy skin
   - Thrombosis
   - Phlebitis
   - Recent scar tissue
   - Bony areas
   - Epilepsy (seek G.P.'s consent)
   - Diabetes (seek G.P.'s consent)
   - Heart condition or disease (seek G.P.s consent)
   - Extremely hairy areas

2. Remove all jewellery and explain the sensation of treatment to your client. If possible pre-heat the area requiring treatment (the tissues are more receptive to treatment if they are warm).

3. It is usual for the client to take a shower before treatment however if this is not possible wipe over the area with cologne or surgical spirit.

4. Test that the machine is in good working order i.e. that the machine is on a stable base, the lead is connected and controls are at zero. Place an appropriate sized ventouse onto your forearm and increase the intensity of suction until you are confident that the machine is operating effectively.

   Place the ventouse in a small bowl of hot soapy water to re-sanitise.

5. Collect the appropriate ventouses from the steriliser.

6. Apply a suitable medium to the area, this is usually a liberal amount of cream or oil which will enable to cup to glide over the area smoothly.

7. Use of the ventouse will vary according to whether your cup has an inlet hole or not. There are two techniques for the gliding cup method:

   Place the cup on the area and gradually adjust the suction until the skin fills no more that 20% of it. Lift and glide in a straight line towards the nearest lymphatic nodes (see Figure 8.8) breaking your suction just before the nodes by either removing your finger from the inlet hole or using your little finger to to depress the skin releasing the cup.

8. Cover the area to be treated overlapping each stroke by half a cup at a time, continue this technique covering the whole area 8-10 times (use skin reaction as a guide).

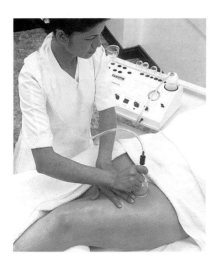
Figure 8.9 Draining to the inguinal nodes using vacuum suction

TIP: Check the ventouse before use and ensure it is smooth around the rim and crack free.

TIP: If pre-heating, reduce the number of strokes to avoid over-working the area.

N.B. if the area has been pre-heated repetitions may be reduced to 6-8 strokes.

9. At the end of treatment, apply manual effluerage movements and remove excess oil or cream from the area.

10. Ensure all your cups and tubes are washed in hot soapy water and dried thoroughly.

Specific Precautions to Vacuum Suction

Bruising may result through poor technique i.e. Over treating an area, pushing the ventouse down on an area, pressure too high and pulling the cup off the skin.

Do not work over thread veins as this treatment will aggravate them.

The multi cup technique is not as popular but may be used for spot treatment. Apply the gliding technique initially, to introduce your client to the treatment. Appropriate cups are positioned and their valves adjusted until a suitable degree of lift is achieved. The unit is switched onto the 'pulse rhythm' and adjusted until the flesh can be seen lifting and relaxing.

The sets of cups will need to be moved at regular intervals inorder to cover the whole of the area requiring treatment. Duration of treatment is usually 10-15 minutes.

Galvanic Body Treatment

Saline is used in the treatment of soft fat and cellulite conditions. It is composed of water and salt (sodium chloride). The charged particles in it are sodium ions (Na^+), which have a positive charge, and chloride ions (Cl^-), which have a negative charge.

Effects

- mobilises subcutaneous tissue
- stimulates cellular metabolism locally
- increases blood flow
- eliminates toxins and waste products.

Preparation and application

1. All equipment should be prepared safely prior to your client's arrival. Electrodes, in particular, should be clean and smooth and should be 1 cm smaller than the sponge glove into which they fit.

2. The client should be comfortably positioned in a lying or semi-reclined position (depending on the area being treated).

3. The treatment must be explained carefully (to include 'prickling' sensation) and the skin sensitivity tests should be carried out on the area requiring treatment.

4. The area to be treated must be clean, grease free and dry.

5. Ensure your client is not contra-indicated.

   ### Contraindications to Body Galvanic Treatment
   - Loss of skin sensation
   - Metal plates, pins, etc
   - Pregnancy
   - Cuts and abrasions
   - Recent scar tissue
   - Abnormally low blood pressure

TIP: Never pull the ventouse cup straight off the skin or apply pressure as not only will you cause your client considerable discomfort but you may also bruise the tissues.

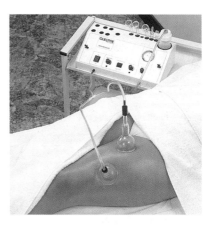

Figure 8.10 Multi cup technique

TIP: This treatment should be taken as a course used in conjunction with exercise and a healthy eating plan.

TIP: The 'pinprick' test ensures that your client would be aware of any concentration of current. The hot and cold test checks the skin's sensitivity.

❝TIP: Place the inactive electrode opposite the active, if possible. ❞

❝TIP: If your client complains of a burning sensation, turn down the current immediately and terminate the treatment. ❞

❝TIP: The area under the pad should be evenly red as a result of the treatment. ❞

❝TIP: Rinse the sponge gloves thoroughly after use to avoid a build up of salt that may bring about a concentration of current. ❞

I Not on abdominal area if client fitted with IUD
I Diseases and disorders of the skin including psoriasis and eczema
I Heart conditions or pacemaker fitted
I Epilepsy (seek G.P'.s consent)
I Diabetes (seek G.P.'s consent).

6. Soak the sponge glove to be placed on the site requiring treatment in 2 per cent saline. Soak the sponge glove to be placed next to or opposite the site requiring treatment in 1 per cent saline. Ensure that the sponges are damp but not dripping.

7. Check that the machine controls are set at zero, then place the pads on your client. The negative electrode in the sponge glove, previously soaked in 2 per cent saline, being the active and the other being inactive. Switch the machine's polarity to negative.

8. Slowly increase the intensity, remembering the principle is 2–3 milliamps per 2 cm square of electrode.

9. The treatment usually takes 15–20 minutes until the desired effect has been achieved, then turn down the intensity and switch the machine off.

10. Reverse the polarity to positive and gradually increase the intensity for 2–5 minutes only.

11. Allow your client to rest for 5 minutes following the treatment.

Dangers and precautions specific to galvanism

Electric shocks

An electric shock may be caused by:

I wet floors and surfaces
I reversing polarity during the treatment
I adjusting the intensity control too quickly
I inadequate earthing of the machinery.

Burns

There are two types of burns – chemical and heat.

Chemical is caused by excessive current and is characterised by raised pink lesions immediately apparent which later turn grey and ooze. If you suspect your client has a chemical burn advise them to see their GP.

Heat is caused by excessive build up of heat which is characterised by redness. There are several causes:

I the skin
  – dry skin is more resistant than wet
  – ischamia
  – freckles
I electrode being uneven in shape or too angular at the corners. Sponge gloves being too damp or evenly wet, worn, torn, creased or too thin. This type of burn may also be caused by a build up of saline in the sponges if they have not been washed thoroughly following treatment
I saline being incorrectly mixed.

Faradic Type Treatment (neuro-muscular electrical stimulation)

This useful body treatment, is particularly effective when combined with active exercise and a healthy eating plan, as it will result in reshaping the

Figure 8.11 Cellulite treatment

body and restoring good muscle tone. It is particularly useful as a post pregnancy treatment to tone the abdominals, and is a useful treatment to use in conjuction with weight loss as it can firm body contours and maintain an attractive looking physique. It can be applied as a spot treament on a specific area or as a general body treatment but must be provided to your client as a course of 12 treatments. (2–3 times per week).

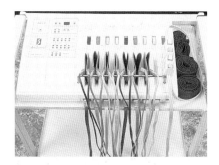

Figure 8.12 Computerised faradic (NMES) machine

Effects

I Stimulation of circulation as the muscles contract which increases the oxygen and nutrient supply to the area.

I Produces erythema (reddness under the pad).

I Increases metabolic rate.

I Stimulates the muscle causing it to contract and acting as a passive form of exercise.

I Strengthens and tones muscle weak muscles.

Comparison with Exercise

With normal exercise you may expect to achieve the stimulation of all bodily functions such as:– respiratory, digestive, heart, co-ordination skills and skin secretions. It should be explained to your client that the above will not be improved or stimulated as there is no joint movement and no effect on fat hence this treatment does not achieve weight loss or the sense of well being usually associated with activity. However, it is in fact, a great boost for those individuals who do not enjoy physical exercise or are unable to take part in physical activity. The best results will be achieved with those clients that combine a plan of specific homecare exercises and a healthy eating plan with this treatment.

Neuro-muscular electrical stimulation for body treatment

Methods of padding up your client are as follows:

I Duplicate motor points padding – uses two pads (one pair of electrodes) placed on two suitably adjacent muscles on one side of the body. It is repeated on the other side of the body.

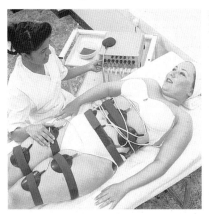

Figure 8.13 Longitudinal padding (front of body)

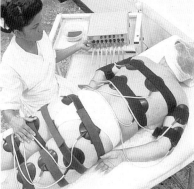

Figure 8.14 Longitudinal padding back)

I Longitudinal padding – uses one pair of electrodes placed on one muscle towards the origin and insertion and is usually repeated on the other side of the body.

I Split padding – uses one pair of electrodes, one placed on the motor point and the other placed on the same muscle on the opposite side of the body.

Application of body treatment

6TIP: This treatment is ideal for those of your clients who do not enjoy exercise and require toning of specific muscle groups.**9**

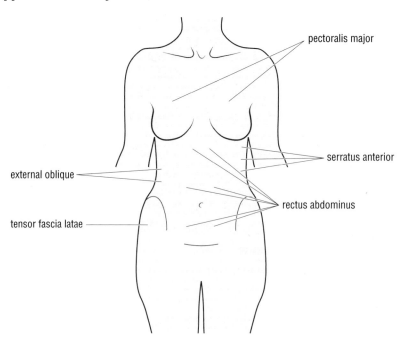

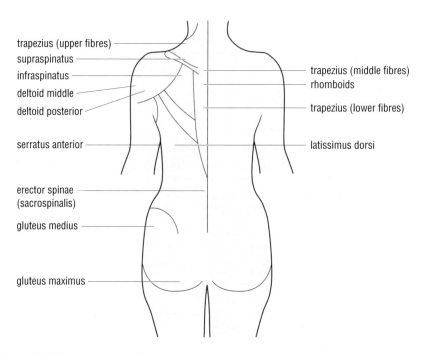

Figure 8.15 Motor points in the body

Application

1. Ensure the client is comfortably positioned on the couch. If your client is on their back, adjust the couch so that they are semi reclined. Ensure that all jewellery is removed

    Check for specific contraindications:

Figure 8.16 Padding up anterior of body

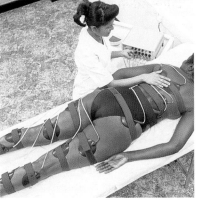

Figure 8.17 Padding up posterior of body

> TIP: Modern machines use an interrupted direct current.

- Disorders and diseases
- Broken skin
- Diabetes (seek G.P.'s approval)
- Epilepsy (seek G.P.s' approval)
- Heart condition
- Muscle injury or disorder of the muscular system
- Recent scar tissue
- Thrombosis
- Phlebitis
- Abnormal blood pressure
- Loss of tactile sensation
- Clients with a nervous disposition
- Pregnancy
- Bony areas
- Metal plates, fillings, pins, pacemaker, bridges or IUD
- Directly over varicose veins
- Acute inflammation.

> TIP: A moist skin will be less resistant to current.

> TIP: Muscles will achieve a better contraction if relaxed, e.g. a semi reclined position would be most applicable for treatment of the abdominals.

2. It is advisable to offer your client a pre heating treatment as their body tissues will be more receptive if warm and any of the following could preceed the treatment: Steam, sauna, infrared, radiant heat or shower. Explain the treatment sensation to your client and carry out the necessary skin sensitivity tests.

3. Check the machine for electrical safety i.e. stability, controls are off or at zero and leads are secure. Ensure that you have all you need at hand so that you do not have to leave your client.

4. Test the machine on your self to check that current is flowing then re-sanitise the electrodes. To do this hold one pair of electrodes between thumb and finger with one hand and turn up the intensity with your free hand until you feel a tingling sensation through the pads.

> TIP: Warm muscles contract more easily than cold ones.

5. Selecting the most suitable padding layout, secure the straps to your client and, using a sponge (moistened with 1% saline), wipe each pad and place on the appropriate muscles.

6. Adjust the machine controls accordingly. Warn your client where to expect to feel the sensation and turn up each outlet one at a time.When all pads are working increase the intensity at each outlet until a visable contraction is seen.

> TIP: If you are unable to get a contraction check that the intensity is high enough.

N.B. Always increase intensity during a contraction.

TIP: Keep the pads clean, a build up on the electrode can prevent a contraction.

7. It may be possible to increase the intensity every 10 minutes. Treatment duration is usually 40 minutes, during this time your client should be kept warm and comfortable.

8. On completion of treatment turn the machine off and controls down to zero. Remove the pads and dry the area under them.

9. Don't forget to instruct your client on homecare exercises and products before they leave the salon.

SUMMARY

This chapter has introduced you to a number of mechanical and electrical body treatments. You now have an overview as well as a knowledge of step by step application. You will appreciate the need to always work with considerable care and with reference to manufacturer's instructions. You should keep yourself up to date with the latest developments in electrical treatments as new treatments are being introduced on a regular basis.

FURTHER STUDY

1. Research the popularity of high frequency treatments in the beauty industry, from your findings answer the following:
   a) How much does a course of treatment cost?
   b) What treatments may be offered in combination with high frequency?

2. Find out about the following areas of sensitivity on the body:
   a) The popliteal fossa
   b) The femoral triangle
   c) The cubital fossa
   and answer the following:
   i) Give the general location and describe the boundaries of the above.
   ii) Explain why care should be taken when working near them.

3. In table form, compare the effectiveness of active exercise with faradic type treatment.

4. Draw up a comparison of audio sonic and percussion vibration treatment.

5. Using your manufacturer's guidelines, explain the purpose of the following controls on the faradic type unit:
   a) Frequency
   b) Pulse width
   c) bi-phasic
   d) mono phasic

6. Why should the relaxation time be as long or longer than the relaxation time set on a faradic type unit?

7. Define the following: elements, compounds, atoms, ions, and electrolytes.

8. Explain briefly, using a diagram, what is meant by a direct current.

9. What is the function of the milliammeter?

10 Describe the risks associated with using uneven pads in a galvanic treatment.

REVEW QUESTIONS

1. Give the purpose of recording the following during a preliminary consultation:

   a) personal details

   b) medical details.

2. Describe the appearance of a varicose vein.

3. Sketch each of the electrodes used in a high frequency treatment and state the use of each.

4. Give four precautionary measures that should be taken when using electrical equipment in the salon.

5. How would you make up a 1% saline solution?

6. Give four reasons for a poor contraction during a faradic type treatment.

7. A client is booked into your salon, she has cellulite on the outer thighs, slack muscle tone on the abdomen and is generally unfit. Plan a course of treatment giving reasons for your selection and state the order in which you would apply them.

8. For each electrical treatment, give one piece of homecare advice you could offer your client.

Electro-epilation

This chapter will provide you with an overview and a step by step guide to the techniques of three methods of epilation. You will be able to compare the features of each technique. To provide a professional service you will need information about consultation and contra-indications which are specific to these techniques. This is supplied in this chapter and you are pointed towards the sources of additional information located elsewhere in this book. Background information about hair and its growth is also provided.

Unit 16a

16a.1 Assess clients and prepare treatment plans

16a.2 Prepare the treatment room and client for epilation

16a.3 Carry out diathermy and blend epilation to meet the treatment plan

Unit 16b

16b.1 Assess clients and prepare treatment plans

16b.2 Prepare the treatment room and client for epilation

16b.3 Carry out diathermy and galvanic epilation to meet the treatment plan

CONTENTS

Introduction	129
Hair	129
Temporary methods of hair removal	134
Electrolysis	135
Electro-epilation	135
Methods of epilation	137
Contra-indications to electro-epilation	142
Probing	143
Needles	143
Re-growth hair	145
Summary	146
Further study	147
Review questions	147

INTRODUCTION

For many years women all over the world have been trying to remove superfluous hair by one method or another. The term used for this is depilation and it covers both temporary and permanent forms of hair removal. Electro-epilation is the term used for a range of techniques that employ electrical current to destroy the hair root. This skill is highly specialised and should be undertaken only when fully competent. Incorrectly performed it can produce skin scarring besides other problems and therefore requires high levels of skill and observance of hygiene procedures. As technology moves forward, it is essential that the beauty therapist providing this service maintains their awareness of these changes.

HAIR

As an electrologist you need a good understanding of the types of hair growth, the structure of hair and follicle and the functions of the hair follicle and hair cycle if you are to formulate an effective treatment plan for your client.

Hairs vary in length, texture and colour depending on which part of the body they grow. They consist largely of the protein keratin, which also forms nails. Hair growth starts in the dermis at the bottom of a long pocket called the follicle, which is lined with epithelium cells. At the bottom of this follicle is a structure called the dermal papilla. Immediately above the dermal papilla the follicle is quite fat and this part is called the hair bulb and encases the dermal papilla. The rest of the hair in this area is known as the hair root and the part which protrudes beyond the skin is called the hair shaft. The hair bulb and the hair root are surrounded by two layers of epithelium cells known as the inner and outer root sheath. Surrounding these two layers of cells is a layer of the dermis, that is, the capillary layer called the connective tissue sheath. At the side of the hair follicle is a small muscle called the erector pili muscle. When contracted this muscle makes the hair stand erect from the skin at an angle, which causes a puckering of the skin to appear known as goose flesh. The hair follicle is fed by a localised blood supply that circulates in minute capillaries in the dermal papilla to bring about hair growth and is rich in amino acids which help to form the protein keratin.

The dermal papilla

This is concave in shape, composed of connective tissue and lies inside the hair bulb. It is the active centre of the matrix region of the hair follicle. The dermal papilla has a permanent capillary in the neuro-vascular network which passes over the bulb of the growing hair follicle and enters the dermal papilla. Most growing hair follicles contain two capillary loops in the upper part of the dermal papilla region. The number of capillary loops in the dermal papilla changes with the size and the shape of the growing hair.

Dermal papilla during the anagen stage

It is large and attached by a narrow stalk to the basal plate of connective tissue, and a basal membrane called the basal lamina separates the dermal papilla from the cells of the hair bulb.

Dermal papilla during the catagen stage

At the onset of the catagen cycle the dermal papilla shrinks, recedes upwards and slips away from its central capillary plexus, lying isolated just below the follicle.

Dermal papilla during the telogen stage

During this stage of the hair cycle the dermal papilla shrinks further, becoming more isolated below the follicle and the capillaries remain collapsed at the base of the telogen follicle in a tangled mass. The capillaries network from any part of the follicle and the sebaceous gland in a continuous system.

Hair bulb

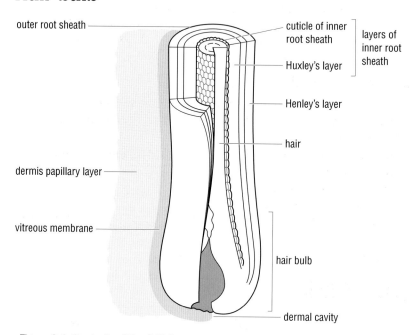

Figure 9.1 The bulb of the follicle

The hair bulb encases the dermal papilla. It is the thickest part of the hair follicle and is onion-shaped in appearance. The hair bulb has two distinct regions: the upper and the lower.

Lower region of the hair bulb

This consists of rapidly dividing and undifferentiated cells of high mitotic activity. It is in this region of the hair bulb that growth and differentiation of the matrix cells start, with the cells of the hair shaft and inner root sheath being formed. The cells move up from the matrix in rows to the upper region of the hair bulb.

Upper region of the hair bulb

In this upper region there is a low rate of mitotic activity. Here the cells differentiate with the matrix cells destined to form the inner root sheath breaking away, moving out and upwards at a more rapid rate than the cells destined to form the cortical cells of the hair shaft.

Outer root sheath

⏐ Location – surrounds the inner root sheath, forms the follicle walls and is a continuation of the basal layer of the epidermis.

| Structure – germinative epithelial cells, which contain water and glycogen. Its thickness varies along its length.

| Function – when stimulated by local blood supply it is the source of the hair-germ cells, which in turn leads to the re-building of the lower follicle structure.
The outer root sheath can be divided into three distinct areas:

| The Upper Region – which lies above the opening duct of the sebaceous gland and is continuous with the stratum corneum of the epidermis.

| The Middle Region – extends from the mouth of the sebaceous gland down to the neck of the hair bulb.

| The Lower Region – surrounds the hair bulb and it is here that the outer root sheath is only two cells thick. It is in this lower region that mitotic activity starts when stimulated by local hormones and enzymes. There is also a connection here with the cells undergoing keratinisation whilst going through differentiation.

The inner root sheath

| Location – lies between the hair shaft and the outer root sheath originating at the base of the follicle until it reaches the level of the sebaceous gland.

| Structure – composed of germinative epithelial cells and has three distinct layers:
  – outer layer – Henley's
  – middle layer – Huxley's
  – inner cuticle layer which interlocks with the outer cuticle of the hair shaft.

| Function – anchors the hair in the follicle.

Types of hair

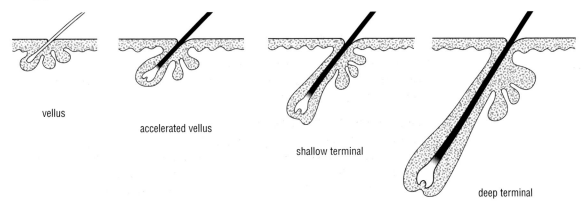

vellus

accelerated vellus

shallow terminal

deep terminal

Figure 9.2 Transition of a vellus follicle to terminal

There are only three types of hair growth:

| lanugo

| vellus

| deep terminal.

Vellus is soft downy fine hair which covers the entire body except for the palms of the hands and the soles of the feet. It is normally without a medulla and is about 2 cm long, growing from the lobe of the sebaceous gland and deriving its nourishment from the same blood supply as the sebaceous gland. These hairs never become terminal hairs unless topical stimulation is applied, as in shaving, plucking, systemic stimulation, hormone changes (puberty, pregnancy, menopause), which induces the follicle to grow downwards for terminal hair growth due to receiving a deep, rich blood supply from the dermis. This change may take place gradually over a period of a few months or years.

Vellus hair has a shedding and replacement growth cycle the same as in terminal hair growth, only at a much slower rate of growth, often taking two or three months to re-appear and remaining in the telogen stage for six to eight months before shedding.

Deep terminal hair growth replaces vellus hairs in certain areas during hormone changes in the life cycle, i.e. puberty, pregnancy, menopause. Terminal hairs are heavily pigmented, coarser in texture and much longer than any other forms of hair. They have a well-developed root, comprising of a bulb matrix and dermal papilla with a rich blood supply. A terminal hair has three distinct layers:

I cuticle

I cortex (colour pigment located here)

I medulla (not always present).

Hair growth cycle

There are three phases of the growth cycle of a hair follicle: anagen, catagen and telogen.

Anagen is the stage of cellular growth and development. It is the first part of the formation of a new hair and new follicle and involves the complete rebuilding of the lower portion of the follicle. The new structure starts forming from the dermal cord, which is a solid column of epithelial hair germ cells that extends downwards from the base of the remnants of the former (old) follicle structure that has previously degenerated and broken down. The dermal cord begins to enlarge when the cells multiply during mitosis, growing in width and length down into the dermis. At the same time the tip of this column of cells (the dermal cord) forms a rounded depression in which the basal dermal papilla cells gather. The structure continues to grow in a downward direction where the lower part of the cord forms the hair bulb, that in turn encases the dermal papilla. Before the follicle reaches its maximum depth, the matrix cells in the lower part of the bulb are made active. It is from the matrix that the new hair cells grow. They form as the cells move upwards from the matrix and begin to differentiate (divide) into two distinct types of cells.

The cells continue to move up in the hair bulb and keratinisation occurs in its upper region, where the inner root sheath rises, pushing its way through the solid cord and forms a protective core for the hair to follow. Once the hair is keratinised it eventually breaks through the apex of the inner root sheath. This occurs about two thirds of the way up the follicle and continues out through the pore as a visible shaft of hair.

An anagen hair when epilated has the appearance of being shiny, moist and pigmented. It has a bulb and inner root sheath present.

Catagen is the transitory, rapidly changing stage of the cycle; it is the complete reversal of anagen. There are approximately 11 per cent of hairs in this stage. It lasts only a very short time, 1–2 weeks.

Catagen is the stage where all mitotic activity has ceased in the matrix and no new cells are produced. The cells in the upper region of the bulb continue to move up the follicle and differentiate into the hair shaft. The usefulness of the hair follicle is now over and the follicle starts to undergo rapid changes. The lower follicle shrinks by one third of its former size and rises up in the dermis. The dermal papilla shrinks and separates and then withdraws from the matrix and rises up in the epidermis. The collapse of the dermal papilla simultaneously triggers the collapse of the hair follicle and the hair bulb, which initiates the undifferentiated cells to move inward to the area of the lower follicle to form the dermal cord which now resembles a disorganised column of cells at the base of the hair follicle. The hair becomes either detached and is shed or remains dormant, lodged in the follicle wall where it derives it nourishment locally and is known as a club hair.

A catagen hair when epilated has a dry, shaggy appearance due to losing water and glycogen.

Telogen is the dormant or resting stage before the shedding of the hair. There are approximately 1 per cent of hairs in this stage. This telogen cycle lasts 3–4 months usually in the terminal hair cycles. The telogen follicle is two-thirds shorter than the anagen follicle as it continues to degenerate further after the catagen phase.

The resting follicle as two distinct regions:

- the area above the level of the sebaceous gland where the cells are similar to the surface epithelium
- the shrunken lower follicle (now called the epithelial sac) where the cells are inactive.

Beneath the follicle the dermal papilla lies greatly shrunken in size as a compact ball of inactive dermal cells and maintains contact with the follicle by means of the epithelial dermal cord. This dermal cord acts in partnership with the inactive dermal papilla and will merge together to build a new follicle when stimulated by the local biochemical processes. The length of time the follicle rests in telogen varies from one area to another and the general characteristics of the individual. However, sometimes the follicle does not rest but is stimulated immediately by the blood supply, hormones and enzymes.

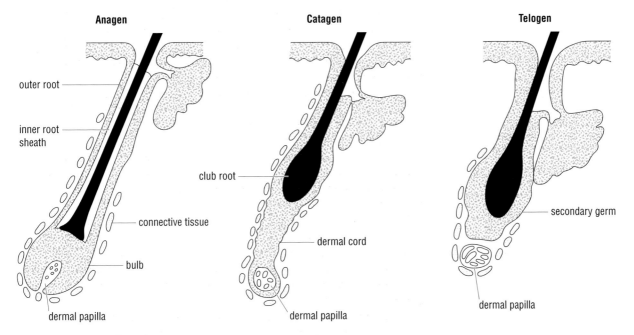

Figure 9.3 Stages of hair growth

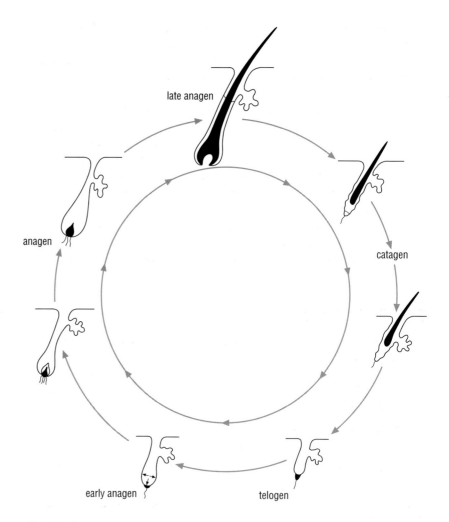

Figure 9.4 Hair growth cycle

TEMPORARY METHODS OF HAIR REMOVAL

It is important for you to establish any previous methods of hair removal used on hair growth presented for electrolysis. This will help you to choose the best possible and most effective treatment for your client. It is therefore essential that you understand the effects of all temporary methods of hair removal on the skin tissue and hair root.

Temporary methods include:

▌ Waxing – probably the best temporary method as it can remove, for 4 to 6 weeks, small to large areas of hair growth in one session without causing stubble or skin damage, and with prolonged use will improve the hair problem.

▌ Shaving – only removes the hair from the skin's surface and is not very effective as hair growth can generally be seen in a few days. It also causes skin tissue to become thickened and sensitised with an erythema and spots forming. Hair texture becomes coarser with compound hair growth resulting and scaring is very common if used regularly on legs.

▌ Depilatory creams – dissolves hair growth by using strong chemical caustic action and, since hair and skin are both composed of keratin, the skin can be adversely sensitised and often left with an erythema background and tender for several hours after treatment. Hair growth may occur from within a few days to two weeks, according to hair type. Prolonged use can lead to an allergic reaction and in some cases can cause dermatitis and localised hyper-pigmentation also occurs given time.

I Plucking – its effect is only to remove hair from the follicle and stimulates further hair growth. Constant plucking can lead to skin surface damage resulting in a bumpy, uneven surface and scar tissue due to infected follicles often occurring as a direct result of plucking and spots forming in treated area. Hair growth in time becomes darker and coarser in texture and becomes more wide spread.

I Sugaring – similar, in principle, to waxing. A sugary substance is applied to the skin and hair and worked in with the fingers and then ripped off the skin taking the hairs out by the root. Works well on fine hair growth with re-growth between 4 to 6 weeks later and fine in texture.

ELECTROLYSIS

Electrolysis is the only permanent method of treatment for the removal of excess facial and body hair growth that is considered socially unacceptable socially for women generally. It is, however, not a miracle cure but a course of regular treatment that varies with each individual according to:

I the type of hair growth

I the cause of hair growth

I how long the hair growth has existed

I any previous temporary methods of hair removal used on this hair growth.

Each hair is treated by a fine needle inserted into a hair follicle (hair root). A mild electric current is then passed down the needle for 2–3 seconds. A warm sensation is felt when the current is discharged. This acts on the germinative tissue (reproducing area) at the base of the follicle so that further hair growth is destroyed or becomes finer and weaker. The treated hair is removed easily from the follicle and the skin feels warm and has a localised erythema. This is a normal reaction to electro-electrolysis.

Electrolysis works by gradually weakening the hair follicle's ability to reproduce new hair growth until the treatment destroys the follicle's ability to grow hair permanently. Initially there is a gradual thinning out of hair growth which is followed by small bald patches until eventually no hair problem exists.

ELECTRO-EPILATION

As a professional electrologist it is essential that you have the right image to present to the general public, as first impressions influence your client's perception of the standard of professional service being offered. For more guidance upon professional appearance and personal hygiene see chapter 4.

The electrologist needs to fully understand legislation applicable to the beauty industry and fully integrate its use into the daily routine to ensure that health and safety is maintained, preventing the risk of cross-infection and meeting legal and professional responsibilities to the beauty industry and the general public. You could otherwise find yourself in breach of one of main pieces of legislation applicable and the risk of losing local authority registration and business. For details of the relevant legislation see chapter 4.

Consultation

You will use both verbal and non-verbal techniques during the consultation. You should have a calming, sympathetic approach towards your client to help soothe any worries and build their self-esteem regarding their individual hair growth problem. This in turn helps the client to relax and speak more freely about their hair problem and for you and your client to build up a productive professional relationship. A more detailed briefing about client consultation is provided in chapter 5.

When consulting with your client before an electro-epilation programme always:

I Ask the client what their hair problem is, even if it appears an obvious problem, never assume they wish a particular area treated, it may lead to the client being embarrassed and probably offended.

I Discuss briefly the hair growth problem. Establish how long the problem has existed and any previous treatments and the frequency of their use.

I Gain your client's permission to carry out a physical examination to determine skin and hair type.

I Explain that electrolysis is a course of treatment which is the only permanent solution to unwanted hair growth and that it works by progressively thinning out the hair problem until only a few hairs remain and then finally none. Also explain that there will be a percentage of re-growth initially and why. It requires personal commitment and time if treatment is to be successful. Confirm that your client understands this and reassure her of your ability and commitment to eradicate the problem. Finally, explain that there are no side effects, for example skin damage, when being treated by a professional, although there will be an initial localised reaction to the skin, such as pinkness and warmth, which will disappear according to skin sensitivity, usually in a few hours.

I Complete the details of the consultation on your client's record card and ask your client to sign, confirming that the details are accurate. Either book a treatment for a later date to meet the client's lifestyle or carry out a short treatment immediately if time permits.

TIP: Answer all questions that your client may have and check their understanding of any information provided.

Work station set up

The following list of equipment is required to carry out electro-epilation:

I trolley/stool/magnifying lamp

I autoclave (see chapter 4)

I epilation unit and electrode

I sharps box (see chapter 4)

I sterilising liquid container (see chapter 4)

I tissues

I selection of needle sizes and lengths

I cotton wool – dry

I medicated swabs

I cleanser – milk

I toner

I eye pads

I dish for cotton wool

I antiseptic aftercare cream/gel

I disposable surgical gloves

I record card/log sheet/pen

I paper bed role for couch and trolley (see chapter 4)

I pedal bin.

Epilation procedure

Procedure common to all techniques:

1. Sterilise all necessary equipment (see chapter 4).

2. Prepare working area – trolley and couch. Adjust the stool to suit your needs.

3. Check that equipment is in good working order.

4. Turn dial on apparatus to zero.

5. Wash you hands (see chapter 4).

6. Consultation with your client:

    a. fill in record card

    b. fill in treatment log plan

    c. discuss treatment procedure

    d. discuss treatment sensation

    e. discuss treatment area

    f. check for contra-indications

    g. determine probable cause of hair growth

    h. discuss re-growth

    i. cost and duration of treatment.

7. Position client and yourself comfortably to enable ease of needle insertion and prevent injury to yourself.

8. Wash and dry hands and apply surgical gloves.

9. Using a magnifier, analyse:

    a. skin type

    b. hair type.

10. Insert correct needle size into the electrode (following manufacturer's instructions).

11. Cleanse the treatment areas (cleanser and toner for face) then with medicated swabs.

12. Offer your client eye covers, if required, for facial work.

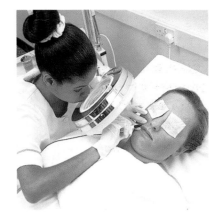

Figure 9.5 Electrologist using illuminated magnifier when working

METHODS OF ELECTRO-EPILATION

There are three methods of epilation:

I Short-wave diathermy – still in use widely (but now competing with the blend combination method).

I Galvanic electrolysis – not used widely nowadays, only as part of the blend technique. Superseded by short-wave diathermy.

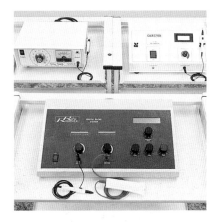

Figure 9.6 Three types of elecrolysis machines

I The blend method – combines both of the previous two mentioned currents and requires more time to treat the hair growth, but produces very effective results with, generally, less re-growth. This technique is becoming increasingly popular with therapists.

Short-wave diathermy electrolysis

Short-wave diathermy (electro-epilation) uses a high-frequency, oscillating, alternating current that produces heat as its destructive force. This current is directed through a fine steel needle probe into the matrix/dermal papilla area of the follicle and discharges for 1 to 2 seconds. The high-frequency energy is absorbed by the water molecules in the cells at the base of the follicle and its effect is to agitate the tissues with heat. This heat breaks down the cellular structure and causes proteins in the cells to congeal as in coagulation and cauterise the blood vessels in the area, either rendering the follicle inactive or weakening its ability to reproduce new hair growth. The surface skin tissues should not be affected if correct treatment procedures and techniques are used. This treatment has the following advantages:

I It is the quickest method of permanent hair removal as an increased number of hairs can be treated in a short period of time compared to galvanic electrolysis or the blend method.

I It is less likely to cause skin damage.

I The skin heals fairly quickly after treatment.

This treatment does, however, produce a high level of re-growth hairs.

Short-wave diathermy procedure

1. Using your magnifier select the darkest and most visible hair growth looking for the angle of hair growth leaving the follicle opening.

2. Switch machine/unit on and adjust current to a minimum amount.

3. Stretch the skin with the index and middle finger of left hand (reverse procedure if left handed) without distorting skin tissue. Place tweezers in between thumb and index finger of left hand (points down).

4. Insert needle under the hair following the direction of hair growth until a resistance is felt.

5. Inform your client when to expect sensation and then discharge current for 2 seconds.

6. Transfer tweezers smoothly into right hand between thumb and index finger maintaining stretch; take hair out of follicle from follicle opening and examine it for stage of hair growth and length of follicle depth; place on tissue.

7. If the hair offers resistance, probe into follicle once more having increased current slightly; it should now fall out easily. If resistance maintained re-evaluate:

   a current intensity

   b. length of current application time

   c. angle of probe.

8. Continue probing the area taking 1 in 4 hairs out to prevent overheating of tissues and to aid the healing process.

9. Complete treatment as per treatment plan.

10. Turn current intensity to zero (if no longer required switch off and unplug).

11. Dispose of contaminated needle in sharps box and waste tissue, cotton wool, etc. in sealed bin liner (see chapter 4).

12. Place tweezers and chuck of electrode into sterilising liquid.

13. Apply aftercare products using a dry cotton wool pad.

14. Brief your client about following homecare advice:

   a no make-up for 24 hours

   b. no heat treatments for 48 hours

   c. no sunbed/sunbathing for 48 hours (could lead to localised hyper-pigmentation)

   d. no swimming/exercise for 24 hours

   e. no tight clothing

   f. no perfumed products

   g. no other treatments to area for 48 hours

   i. management of hair growth between treatments – to use nail scissors only to trim hair growth, this will not interfere with treatment.

15. Ask your client to rest for two minutes whilst aftercare products are absorbed into the skin tissues. Complete record card/log sheet.

16. Tidy trolley.

17. Wash your hands and dry.

18. Show client finished result and confirm their satisfaction.

19. Show your client to reception, process bill and any aftercare products. Book client's next treatment (see chapter 3).
   Points to remember:

   | always check the equipment before use and sterilise tweezers, etc.

   | always use a illuminated magnifying lamp

   | always stretch the skin around the area being treated

   | always insert needle underneath the hair, for ease of insertion

   | always insert at the same angle that the hair grows – to ensure correct insertion 3 mm from follicle mouth determines the angle.

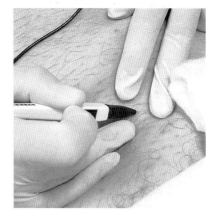

Figure 9.7 Working position

TIP: Health and safety. At the end of the working day or when the bin is full, double wrap and seal bin liner.

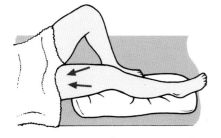
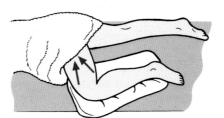

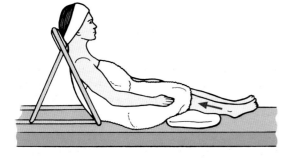
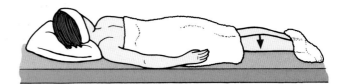
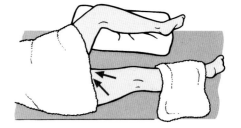

Figure 9.8 Leg working positions

Galvanic chemical electrolysis

This is the oldest form of electrolysis and has now been superseded by short-wave diathermy (electro-epilation). Galvanic electrolysis involves a direct current which possesses polarity because it flows in one direction only through a circuit. To achieve this the current needs one negative (cathode) and one positive (anode) pole for a circuit to be completed. It works on the principle of producing a movement of ions in the skin tissues from negative to positive.

During galvanic electrolysis the client is connected to the indifferent (anode) electrode, which may be covered with a damp lint, and placed in their hand and in turn is attached to the positive outlet on the electrolysis unit. The needle holder/electrode is connected to the negative outlet and is therefore negatively charged. The needle is inserted into the (electrolyte) hair follicle and skin tissues that contain body salts and moisture. When the direct current comes into contact with these body salts and moisture it causes the salt and water to split into their chemical elements (molecules), which then rearrange themselves to form entirely new substances.

The body salts separate into electrically charged ions which react with water, combining with a hydroxyl ion and forming (Lye) sodium hydroxide. This chemical is a highly caustic alkali which results in tissue distruction. This chemical action is not instantaneous but takes time to build up in the tissues and depends upon two factors:

I current intensity

I duration of application time.

Fine hair may require up to 20 seconds, whereas deep, coarse terminal hair may require up to several minutes treatment time to be effective. The treatment does not cease when the current is stopped as chemical action will continue to build up in the tissues for a short time afterwards. Therefore leave the hair for a few minutes (treating other hairs in the area) before removing it, hence it consumes up to several minutes treatment time. If froth appears on the skin's surface, the needle must be wiped free of it to prevent skin damage occurring as if it is left current will travel onto surface tissues.

The direct current has a wide heating pattern and is available along the whole length of the needle but it affects tissue only where moisture is present. The structure of the skin is such that only the deeper layers of the skin contain moisture. The skin's moisture gradient makes it possible to concentrate the treatment at the lower follicle. Sebum is a natural insulator and in turn protects the surface layer of the epidermis.

Galvanic procedure

Prepare you client as for procedure common to all techniques (see page 137). Pass the indifferent/inactive electrode to your client to hold. Follow steps 1 to 19 as for short-wave diathermy procedure (pages 138–139). The duration of current discharge will vary for galvanic from epilation.

Blend epilation

This method has become very popular during the 1990s due to its effectiveness on hair growth. It combines both diathermy and galvanic currents using the best of both currents to destroy the germinative area. The 'blend' is able to treat any type of hair follicle including the most difficult, distorted follicles due to the heating pattern affecting the entire lower follicle area. The heating pattern has a wide field of radiation and travels the length of the lower follicle rather than being concentrated to the area around the tip of the needle.

Re-growth is minimal, however, treatment is longer (up to 5 seconds per hair) and the cost is higher due to this factor.

The electrical currents may be used separately, if required, as well as combined in the one needle. The 'blend' uses a minimal level of diathermy current with higher levels of galvanic current as the main destructive force. The function of the diathermy current is to produce heat in the follicle as the (Sodium Hydroxide) lye is produced, this speeds up its chemical action, making it more caustic, leading to chemical decomposition of the hair growth and destruction of the germinative tissues. This results in very little re-growth compared to using each current separately.

There are a variety of 'blend' units on the market today and each varies; therefore manufacturer's instructions should always be followed to enable you to provide the best possible treatment for your client.

> **TIP:** If you are uncertain about correct procedures, discreetly seek guidance from your supervisor.

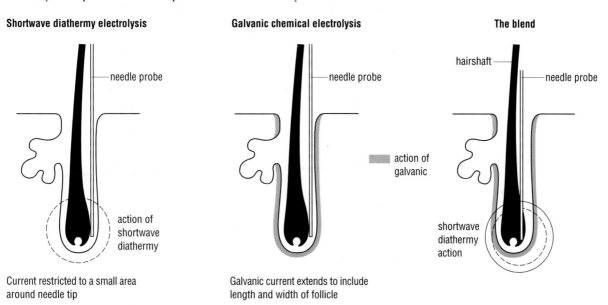

Shortwave diathermy electrolysis

needle probe

action of shortwave diathermy

Current restricted to a small area around needle tip

Galvanic chemical electrolysis

needle probe

action of galvanic

Galvanic current extends to include length and width of follicle

The blend

hairshaft

needle probe

shortwave diathermy action

Figure 9.9 Patterns of tissue destruction

Blend procedure

Prepare your client as for procedure common to all techniques (see page 137).

1. Switch on the blend unit with both currents. Set current to minimum and timer to 5 seconds.

2. Stretch the skin using your index and middle finger of your left hand (reverse procedure if you are left handed) without distorting skin tissues. Place tweezers between your thumb and index finger of left hand (points down).

3. Insert the needle under the hair following the direction of hair growth until resistance is felt.

4. Tell your client when to expect the treatment sensation and then discharge the current for 5 full seconds. If traction is felt, gradually increase the galvanic current intensity until hairs epilate easily; you should ensure intensity is in your client's tolerance level.

5. Remove all treated hairs from follicles and place these on a tissue for disposal. Adjust the current intensity for galvanic when changing areas and working on different hair types.

6. Complete the treatment as per stages 8 to 19 of short-wave diathermy procedure on pages 138–139.

The normal skin reaction following the blend is an erythema – individual follicles may appear slightly raised, swollen and warm. Generally the reaction disappears within an hour, depending on skin type.

CONTRA-INDICATIONS TO ELECTRO-EPILATION

Although a contra-indication is a condition that prevents the therapist from carrying out the treatment, there are many contra-indications that are treatable provided medical advice is sought.

I Heart disorders – rarely causes problems with treatment but should always be referred for medical approval due to the variety of heart conditions.

I Pacemaker – high frequency current may affect the rhythm of the unit, therefore no treatment to be given.

I Epilepsy – treatable if the condition has been controlled by medication and GP gives permission.

I Diabetes – diabetic skins have a slower healing rate and are prone to skin eruptions and infections and therefore should be treated with extra care after medical approval has been given.

I Hepatitis B – is highly contagious and like HIV viruses can be transmitted via body fluids and blood. You should seek medical advice as to whether or not the GP thinks treatment should go ahead. It is recommended that all electrologists/therapists are vaccinated against Hepatitis B.

I Cardiovascular disorders – needs to be referred to a GP due to the type of medication, as anti-coagulant drugs can affect success of the treatment process, according to their strength and side affects of medication.

I Loss of tactile sensation – it is important that your client can respond to hot and cold sensation in the treatment area to ensure correct current intensity, etc. is used and to prevent convergence of heat which leads to skin damage.

I Hairy moles – can be treated but need GP permission due to the nature of the moles.

I Skin disorders/diseases – any condition that may be contagious or infectious prohibits treatment.

I Pregnancy – abdomen or breast areas should not be treated during pregnancy as these areas are tender.

I Drugs – certain medications can adversely affect electrolysis treatment, particularly steroid drugs. It is therefore necessary for the electrologist to establish the nature of the drugs and their affects on the hair growth, skin type, etc.

I Cuts, abrasions, bruising, etc. – these areas should be avoided.

I Emotional problems – if your client is having severe emotional problems this will affect the treatment plan/programme as the client's pain threshold may be low and treatment time may have to be shorter.

TIP: If in doubt as to whether or not to treat your client, always defer and seek medical advice.

PROBING

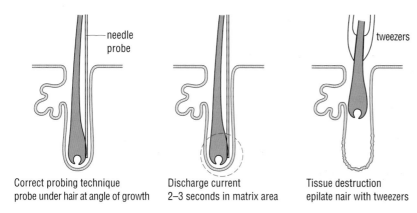

Figure 9.10 Probing procedure

Always choose a pre-packed sterile needle to suit the type of area being treated, that is, face or legs, as this determines the size of the needle to be used. Using sterile tweezers, the needle should be inserted into the needle holder and the machine and checked for any faults prior to use. The needle holder is always held between the thumb and index finger. It should be held firmly but gently and feel comfortable to the operator. The tweezers should always be held between the thumb and index finger of the left hand for ease of change over sequence, and the index finger and middle finger of this hand help to stretch the skin being treated and thus reduces your client's discomfort.

You should, on the insertion of the needle, always try to achieve a smooth and steady insertion into the hair follicle, which should be neither too fast nor too slow to enable you to build up a 'sense of touch'. This is essential when probing the follicle as there is a 'natural resistance' present and the hair follicle is an invisible target.

To help you to probe correctly you must first determine the direction of the hair growth and the angle at which the hair emerges from the hair follicle. If you have done this correctly, when you insert the needle probe underneath the hair it should slide smoothly into the follicle alongside the hair root and feel comfortable to you and your client.

NEEDLES

One of the most important pieces of equipment that you as the electrologist have is your needles. Each needle determines the result achieved and the skin reaction of your client.

All needles should be inspected prior to use under an illuminated magnifier and damaged or faulty ones disposed of in a sharps box. The needle should be of the correct size to enter the follicle, that is, the same diameter as the hair. The needle point should be rounded and bright for ease of insertion.

The depth of the hair being treated determines the length of the needle to be used as the needle must be long enough to reach the germinative layer of the hair follicle. Normally the larger diameter hairs and faster growing hairs have the deepest follicle, whilst the smaller diameter hairs and slower growing hairs have the most shallow follicles.

Today's needles come in varying lengths, standard and extra long, and it is safer to select a needle that is too long rather than too short.

l Insufficient length of current application time – is a common fault when treating re-growth hairs, failing to use sufficient current intensity or its length of application time being too short. Early anagen hairs epilate easily due to lying so shallow in the follicle, but still require sufficient current and application time if constant re-growth is not to occur.

l If most of the re-growth is lying deep in the follicle then your previous probing technique was probably incorrect – too shallow or insufficient current intensity or its application time was too short.

l If most of the re-growth is shallow it may be due to over-probing. This occurs when there are two hairs in the same follicle: an old telogen hair visible on the skin's surface and a new anagen hair in the lower follicle. The operator bypasses the root of the telogen hair and discharges the current lower down the follicle. When epilating the old telogen hair, there is only slight traction due to the follicle being shallow and the hair being ready to shed naturally soon. Therefore probing needs to be adjusted and each hair examined carefully when first starting treatment.

l Missed hairs – hairs that have been passed over (due to being too short, or lying under the skin, or being too fine at the time of treatment) while treating the more noticeable hair growth or just missed out. This type of re-growth will appear the same in diameter and colour and be coarse in texture as the hairs originally treated in this area because they have never received treatment.

l Thinning out – advise your client that to treat all the hairs from one area in one session would, in some cases, be too painful and/or too damaging to the skin tissues due to over treating. Therefore, hairs are treated at random, thinning them out, taking the darkest and thickest first. This gives immediate improvement to the areas and enables you to thin out the finer hair growth in later sessions. This does mean, of course, that there will be a percentage of re-growth and missed hairs at some stage of the treatment. However, the danger of skin damage through over working the area is drastically reduced.

TIP: Always check the re-growth and re-evaluate your technique at regular intervals if you are to maintain a high standard of workmanship.

Re-growth is important as it helps to:

l determine your client's next appointment (due to the stage of the hair growth)

l assess the accuracy of your technique and vary it if there is a higher than expected re-growth level.

It is essential that during the consultation time and first treatment you explain to your client that there will be re-growth, when it can be expected and how it will differ from previous hair growth. Also clearly explain about the missed hairs and when they are due to appear. This will prevent your client becoming despondent at a later date.

SUMMARY

You will have determined from this chapter the need to have a good understanding of the various forms of electrolysis if you are to analyse information received during oral and physical consultation and formulate the most effective treatment programme to meet your client's requirements. You should be able to explain treatment procedures and be confident and competent in all aspects of treatment.

The industry requires you to keep a high level of professionalism and maintain hygiene and safety procedures throughout the treatment.

FURTHER STUDY

1. List the five factors that influence the heating patterns produced in short-wave diathermy.

2. Research the advantages and disadvantages of using the 'flash' technique in short-wave diathermy.

3. Design an electrolysis record card to cover client range, treatment areas, hair type, and any other information you feel is relevant in helping you formulate an effective treatment programme for your client.

4. Produce a leaflet giving clear and brief explanation of electrolysis, homecare and hair growth management procedures to be followed during a course of treatment.

5. Produce a comparison chart of advantages of consultation for the client and the electrologist.

6. Consider what treatment procedures may need to be adapted/modified if treating a black skin.

7. Investigate and report on seven causes of hair growth.

8. Investigate five hormones which either inhibit or stimulate hair growth.

Review questions

1. Name the two methods of sterilisation used for pre-packed disposable needles.

2. State how you would dispose of your contaminated needle.

3. List four factors which determine current intensity.

4. Name the new type of needle available which prevents cross infection via the needle cap.

5. Why should all electrologists use a illuminated magnifier when carrying out electrolysis?

6. List four possible causes of re-growth.

7. State which types of current is used in galvanic electrolysis.

8. Name the destructive force of short-wave diathermy.

9. Consider why it is important for the client to observe hygiene and homecare advice given to them.

10. How would you adapt your treatment if a hair was resistant and the client was unable to take the current any higher (include after treatment)?

10 Aromatherapy massage

This chapter will provide you with the knowledge of essential oils that is so necessary for working safely in this exciting area. You will be able to select appropriate oils for use with your client and be familiar with any contra-indications to their use. You will be aware of safe working practices and how to evaluate the effectiveness of treatments.

Unit 17

17.1 Assess clients and prepare treatment plans

17.2 Prepare for aromatherapy body massage

17.3 Massage the body using aromatherapy techniques

17.4 Gain feedback from clients and advice on aftercare

CONTENTS

Introduction   149

Essential oils   149

Unsafe oils and precautions   151

How oils work   153

Choosing oils for your client   157

Applying aromatherapy massage   161

Evaluating your treatment   163

Summary   164

Further study   165

Review questions   165

INTRODUCTION

Aromatherapy is a treatment that combines the benefits of massage with the therapeutic properties of essential oils. It is a holistic therapy addressing physical and emotional issues on an individual basis – no two clients will receive the same treatment. It promotes a sense of well-being that will encourage your client's own powers of recovery and regeneration. Working in a beauty therapy setting you will not, of course, be attempting to deal with medical problems, but you can make an important contribution to each client's health and happiness.

ESSENTIAL OILS

What are essential oils?

Essential oils are found in very small amounts in various parts of aromatic plants and are what gives the plant its characteristic scent. For example, lavender essential oil is found in the flowering tops, eucalyptus in the leaves and young twigs, rose in the flower petals, lemon in the rind of the fruit, frankincense in the resin, sandalwood in the heartwood of the tree, juniper in the berries, cinnamon in the bark, coriander in the seeds and vetiver in the roots. Essential oils are unlike other oils in that they are volatile, that is, they evaporate when exposed to the air. They do not feel oily and generally do not leave a stain. Many of them are watery in consistency and either colourless or range from pale yellow to pale green.

Extraction

When separated from the bulk of the plant material they are very strong and concentrated, and must be used in very small quantities with great care. The main methods of extraction are water and steam distillation, solvent extraction and expression.

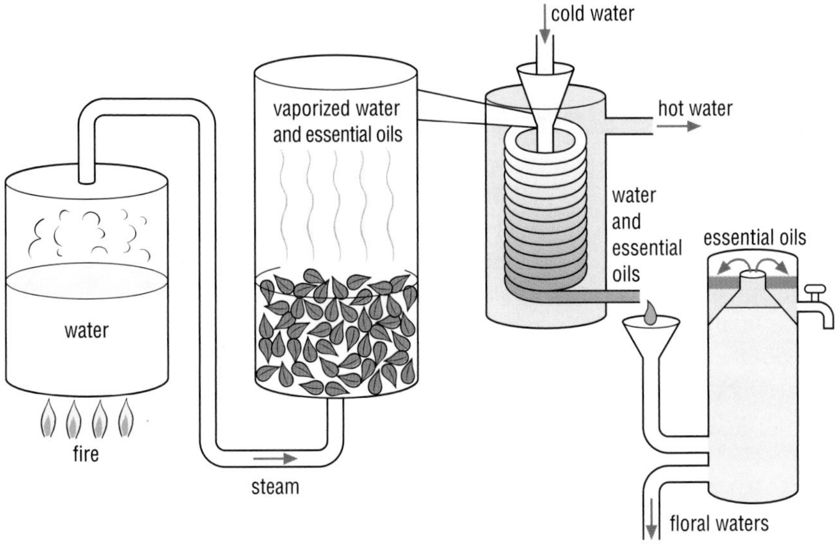

> **TIP**: You will need to research the methods of extraction and how they are carried out – see this chapter's further study section.

Figure 10.1 Distillation

Some oils are more easily extracted than others and some are present in greater quantities in the plant. For example, 100 kg of lavender yields 3 kg of essential oil, while 1000 kg of rose petals yields 300 grams of essential oil. This explains the wide variety in the price of oils.

Chemical structure

The essential oils are enormously complex. Each one is a mixture of hundreds of different compounds almost all of which are made up of unique combinations of either carbon and hydrogen, or these two plus oxygen. This means that, like all living things, they are organic substances produced in the plant by the combination of carbon dioxide from the air and water from the ground in the presence of sunlight. This is known as photosynthesis.

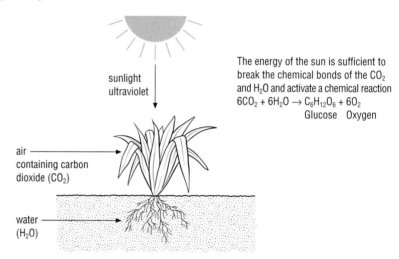

sunlight
ultraviolet

The energy of the sun is sufficient to break the chemical bonds of the CO_2 and H_2O and activate a chemical reaction
$$6CO_2 + 6H_2O \rightarrow C_6H_{12}O_6 + 6O_2$$
Glucose   Oxygen

air
containing carbon
dioxide (CO_2)

water
(H_2O)

Figure 10.2 Photosynthesis

Usually, an essence will have a few major constituents and a large number of trace elements. Thus attempts to reproduce them in the laboratory can never work entirely and synthetic oils do not have the properties of real ones. When you have understood this, you will see how it is possible for one oil to have so many different properties and effects, and how complex are the effects of blending oils together. The chemical constitution of an oil may give us some guidance about its properties and effects – see further study section.

Buying and storing

You will also need to understand how important it is to buy good quality oils, where you can be confident of their purity and freshness. There are many reputable suppliers who belong to the Essential Oils Trade Association (EOTA). They will give you all the information you may want about the composition and quality of the products they supply.

It is vital to store your essential oils correctly, so that they do not deteriorate. Containers must be made of materials that will not interact physically or chemically with them, for example glass NOT plastic.

They must have airtight caps or contents will be lost through evaporation. Exposure to air also hastens the oxidation process which causes irreversible and disastrous changes to the composition, ruining the aroma and therapeutic usefulness.

They must be protected from light, which speeds up the reactions causing deterioration. Amber glass will give adequate protection, but it is wise to store your oils in the dark. They must also be kept cool. The rate of deterioration is doubled for every 10° C rise in temperature. Most oils are best stored in a refrigerator. Some will solidify at this temperature and must be warmed naturally at room temperature before use.

Figure 10.3 Oil bottles with droppers and caps

It is generally thought that, if stored correctly, most oils will have a shelf-life of two years. Your supplier will give you further information. However, the citrus oils (for example lemon) deteriorate much more quickly, possibly in six months, as they are prone to oxidation. They become cloudy and should never be used on the skin in this condition as they can produce severe irritation.

UNSAFE OILS AND PRECAUTIONS

The number of essential oils available to aromatherapists is increasing all the time. It is wise to be cautious about using 'new' oils until safety data are available for them. Listed below are a number of oils that are considered totally unsafe for aromatherapy, plus further lists of other oils for which there are specific precautions with which you need to be very familiar. You must realise that these are powerful substances to be treated with respect.

Health and Safety: essential oils should never be taken internally. They should be kept well away from children due to the risk of personal injury from misuse and kept away from the eyes. They should never be applied neat to the skin. There are a few exceptions under specific circumstances, for example lavender. Do not do it unless you are very sure it is safe. A hypersensitivity test may be used to determine this – if in doubt do not use.

Oils not to be used in therapy

Almond (bitter)	Fennel (bitter)	Sassafras
Boldo Leaf	Horseradish	Savin
Calamus	Jaborandi Leaf	Savory
Camphor	Mugwort	Southernwood
Cassia	Mustard	Tansy
Cinnamon Bark	Origanum	Thuja
Clove	Penny Royal	Wintergreen
Costus	Pine (dwarf)	Wormseed
Elecampane	Rue	Wormwood

In addition, there are concerns about the safety of the following oils, which should therefore also be avoided although they have valuable therapeutic properties:

- Aniseed
- Hyssop
- Sage.

Oils not to be used during pregnancy

These oils could harm the mother or cross the placenta and harm the foetus:

- Basil
- Clary Sage
- Hyssop
- Juniper
- Marjoram
- Myrrh
- Sage

151

Avoid during the first 3–4 months of pregnancy and use cautiously thereafter:

l Fennel (sweet)

l Peppermint

l Rose

l Rosemary

l Chamomile (Roman)

l Frankincense.

Some aromatherapists advocate a much more cautious approach, suggesting that only a limited number of oils in low dilutions are suitable for pregnant and breast feeding women – see further study section.

Oils not to be used for those with high blood pressure

l Hyssop

l Rosemary

l Sage

l Thyme.

Oils not to be used for those suffering from epilepsy

l Fennel

l Hyssop

l Rosemary

l Sage.

Photosensitisation

The following oils render the skin more sensitive to ultraviolet light and so should not be used before exposure to sun or sunbeds:

l Angelica Root

l Bergamot

l Cumin

l Grapefruit

l Lemon

l Lime

l Orange

l Tagetes

l Verbena.

Skin irritants

To be used with care in low dilutions in the bath but safe in massage. Not for those with sensitive skin or allergic reactions. Dilute in a carrier.

l Basil

l Lemon

l Lemongrass

l Lemon Verbena

l Melissa

l Peppermint

l Thyme.

There is also some doubt about Tea Tree, but it could be because contaminated examples have flooded the market.

The following may irritate in massage or baths; cautions as above, not more than 2 per cent dilution in massages (dilutions will be explained later in the chapter):

I Cinnamon Leaf

I Fennel (sweet)

I Fir Needle (Siberian)

I Parsley Seed

I Pimenta Leaf

I Thyme.

Sensitisation and allergies

You must always take particular care with any client who suffers from allergies or asthma or has a family history of such complaints. Any allergic reaction to an oil, usually redness or itching, will develop very quickly – it may be immediate and certainly in 24 hours. With sensitivity, however, it takes 5–7 days for the reaction to develop, after that any contact with any amount of that substance will cause a reaction.

Homeopathic medication

If your client is taking homeopathic medicine you must ask them to check with their homeopath which essential oils should not be used. It is thought that the stronger smelling oils, such as eucalyptus and peppermint, antidote such medication and some homeopaths believe that all the essential oils will do this.

HOW OILS WORK

Essential oils can be used in several different ways. They can be diluted in a base oil or cream and applied to the skin in massage, or in face creams and body lotions. They can be inhaled in steam or directly from a tissue. They can also be added to the bath.

The molecules which make up the essential oils are extremely small and so can penetrate the skin. They are absorbed into the smallest blood capillaries and circulated around the body. At the same time they are breathed in and their smell is experienced. Olfaction (the sense of smell) is closely connected with other functions such as memory, emotional responses and linked body feelings. This is due to the close connection between the area of the brain which registers smell and the limbic system, an older part of the brain in evolutionary terms which controls many of the involuntary aspects of our behaviour; for example, the experience of pain, pleasure, anger, fear, sorrow, sexual feelings and affection.

TIP: You will need to learn how to carry out patch tests to determine whether an oil is safe to use with a sensitive client (see further study section).

Figure 10.4 Inhalation of vapour

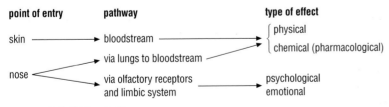

Figure 10.5 Table of effect

Again, you can see how powerful the essential oils can be in their effects.

TIP: It is useful to know the botanical name of the oil, which is in Latin, because there may be several varieties of an oil available and this identifies which one you are getting.

Oil profiles

Let us now look at a selection of essential oils in more detail. There is always more to learn about any particular oil, and once you have got these under your belt you will need to move on to some of the many other useful oils that are available (see further study section for suggestions).

Black Pepper (*Piper nigrum*)

A perennial woody vine grown chiefly in India, Sri Lanka, Indonesia, Malaysia and Madagascar. The oil, which is colourless to slightly bluish-green, is extracted by steam distillation from the dried immature berries. Its character is warming and stimulating.

Main uses: poor circulation, muscular aches and pains, colds and flu, lethargy and mental fatigue.

Safety: can irritate the skin, use in low concentrations.

Family: spice (see blending section).

Camomile (Roman) (*Chamaemelum nobile*)

Daisy-like flowers cultivated mainly in England, Belgium, Hungary, USA, Italy and France. The oil, which is pale blue turning yellow on keeping, is steam distilled from the flower heads. Another type, German Camomile, is bright blue. It is very expensive, but a superior skin care remedy. Its character is soothing and calming without depressing and it is particularly useful with children.

Main uses: skin care, menstrual pain and PMS, headache, insomnia, stress-related complaints, digestive problems and children's complaints.

Safety: do not use in the first three months of pregnancy, can cause skin irritation, use in low concentrations.

Family: flower/herb.

Clary Sage (*Salvia sclarea*)

A biennial or perennial herb up to one metre in height with large hairy leaves and small blue flowers. Mainly cultivated in the Mediterranean. The colourless or pale yellowish-green oil is extracted by steam distillation from the flowering tops. Its character is uplifting and relaxing mentally and emotionally.

Main uses: muscular aches and pain, irregular menstruation and PMS, migraine, depression, stress-related disorders and mental fatigue.

Safety: not to be used in pregnancy. It is thought to produce a narcotic effect when used in conjunction with alcohol.

Family: flower.

Eucalyptus (*Eucalyptus globulus*)

A tall evergreen tree native to Australasia, now cultivated world-wide. The oil is colourless and extracted by steam distillation from fresh or partially dried leaves and young twigs. Its character is stimulating, cooling and decongesting.

Main uses: the classic remedy for respiratory complaints, where it is anti-viral, bactericidal and decongestant, also muscular aches and pains, skins infections, headaches and poor circulation.

Safety: highly toxic taken internally. May irritate sensitive skin.

Family: tree.

Frankincense (*Boswellia carteri*)

A small tree or shrub which yields natural oleogum resin when incisions are made in the bark. It is mainly produced in Somalia, Ethiopia, China and Saudi Arabia. The pale yellow or greenish oil is steam distilled from selected oleogum resin. Its character is warming, calming, relaxing and revitalising.

Main uses: skin care (especially ageing), respiratory complaints (especially asthma as it helps to deepen the breath), menstrual problems, anxiety and stress-related disorders.

Safety: advisable to avoid in first three months of pregnancy.

Family: resin.

Geranium (*Pelargonium graveolens*)

A perennial shrub up to one metre high with serrated leaves and small pink flower, grown chiefly in Reunion, Egypt, Russia and China. The yellowish-green to greenish-olive oil is steam distilled from the leaves, stalks and flowers. Its character is harmonising, balancing, refreshing and uplifting.

Main uses: skin care (all skin types as it balances sebum production), cellulite, poor circulation, water retention, menstrual problems, PMS, nervous tension and stress-related disorders.

Safety: may irritate very sensitive skin.

Family: herb.

Juniper Berry (*Juniperus communis*)

A small evergreen conifer with bluish-green prickly needles producing bluish-black berries, grown commercially chiefly in Eastern Europe, France, Italy, Austria, Germany and Canada. The virtually colourless oil is steam distilled from the berries. Avoid inferior grade of juniper extracted from leaves and wood or fermented berries that have been used to make gin. Its character is uplifting to the spirits yet warming and calming. It is cleansing and detoxifying.

Main uses: any condition where there is a build up of toxins, e.g. rheumatism, arthritis, cellulite, infections of the urinary tract, skin infections, anxiety, nervous tension and stress-related conditions.

Safety: not to be used in pregnancy, may irritate sensitive skins, not to be used with any client who has kidney problems.

Family: tree.

Lavender (*Lavandula augustifolia*)

An evergreen woody shrub bearing bluish-mauve flowers in spikes. It is native to the Mediterranean though now cultivated world-wide. Most of the colourless to pale yellow oil is produced in France, Spain and Bulgaria by steam distillation from the fresh flowering tops. Its character is balancing for mind and body, calming and soothing while uplifting and refreshing.

Main uses: skin care, infections and irritations, respiratory infections, muscular aches and pains, digestive problems, PMS, depression, headaches, tensions, insomnia, migraine, shock and stress-related condition. It boosts the immune system and protects against disease and infection. It is an extremely versatile oil.

Safety: although it can be used neat on the skin unlike other oils, there are reports of skin irritation from over use.

Family: flower/herb.

Lemon (*Citrus limon*)

A small evergreen tree cultivated extensively world-wide. Most of the pale yellow oil is produced in Italy, Cyprus, Israel and California by cold expression of the fruit and peel. Its character is uplifting and tonic.

Main uses: it is strongly antiseptic and anti-viral so used against skin infections, colds and flu. It stimulates the circulation and digestion. When added to blends it is thought to enhance the properties of the other oils.

Safety: it is photo toxic and may cause skin irritation or sensitivity, use in low concentration. It is prone to oxidation and more likely to irritate when this has occurred.

Family: citrus.

Petitgrain (*Citrus aurantium var amara*)

The oil is nowadays produced from many varieties and hybrids of orange and lemon trees, mostly in Paraguay, although supplies from Italy, Egypt and Tunisia are thought to be superior. It is pale yellow to amber and extracted by steam distillation from the leaves and young twig tips. Its character is refreshing and uplifting.

Main uses: care of oily skin and hair, indigestion and flatulence, insomnia, anxiety and depression, PMS, nervous exhaustion and stress-related conditions.

Safety: no cautions.

Family: citrus.

Rose (*Rosa centifolia* and *Rosa damascena*)

There are two forms of the oil. Rose otto is obtained by steam distillation from the petals. It is virtually colourless and extremely expensive. The less expensive rose absolute is a viscous (thick), yellowish-orange liquid obtained by solvent extraction from the fresh petals. Oil from *R. centifolia* (Cabbage Rose) comes mainly from Morocco, Tunisia, Italy, France and China, while oil from *R. damascena* (Damask Rose) comes from Turkey and France, and the best is from Bulgaria. Its character is warming, calming and supportive.

Main uses: rose is thought to enhance and support female energy, it is helpful for sexual problems, period problems, uterine disorders and skin disorders. It supports the heart both physically and emotionally and helps with depression, nervous tension and stress-related conditions.

Safety: avoid in the first three months of pregnancy.

Family: flower.

Rosemary (*Rosmarinus officinalis*)

A shrubby evergreen bush with needle-shaped leaves and small pale blue flowers native to the Mediterranean and cultivated world-wide. The colourless to pale yellow oil is produced mainly in Morocco, France and Spain by steam distillation of the flowering tops. Its character is stimulating, refreshing, warming and invigorating.

Main uses: respiratory ailments, muscular aches and pains, poor circulation, aiding concentration and memory, digestive disorders, weakness and exhaustion, stimulating the nerves.

Safety: avoid during pregnancy. Do not use with epileptics or those suffering from high blood pressure. It may irritate sensitive skins.

Family: herb.

Sandalwood (*Santalum album*)

An evergreen tree with leathery leaves and small pinkish-purple flowers which is native to tropical Asia and especially Mysore in India where the best quality oil is produced. It is a pale greenish-yellow or brownish-yellow viscous oil obtained by steam distillation of the roots and heartwood. Its character is cool and decongestant, and soothing.

Main uses: skin care, especially for cracked and chapped skin, respiratory disorders especially throat problems, urinary tract infections, nausea, PMS, depression, tension and stress.

Safety: no cautions.

Family: tree.

Tea Tree (*Melaleuca alternifolia*)

A small tree with small needle-like leaves, native to Australia, especially New South Wales. The pale yellowish-green to colourless oil is steam distilled from the leaves and twigs. It character is cooling and head clearing. It also combats all forms of infection and stimulates the immune system.

Main uses: skin infections, athletes foot, warts, respiratory disorders, flu, thrush, cystitis and gastro-enteritis.

Safety: can be irritating to people with sensitive skins and those prone to allergies, particularly if used neat or in high concentrations.

Family: tree.

CHOOSING OILS FOR YOUR CLIENT
Consultation

This is your opportunity to get as much information as you need from your client in order to give them the best possible treatment, to answer any questions about what aromatherapy involves and to make sure that the expectations of the effects of treatment are realistic. You should use this time to build a rapport with your client. The more you can do this the more your client will relax and trust you, and the more beneficial the treatment will be.

Within aromatherapy treatment you are more directly concerned with your client's sense of well being and emotional state than you would be when giving, for example, an electrical body treatment and this needs to be reflected in the questions you ask in your consultation. Your salon may already use an aromatherapy consultation card, but if not think about what you want to know and design your own. If there is one and it does not cover everything, add supplementary questions. Consultation is a skill that, like any other, will improve with experience. Any counselling skills you can learn will be a great help. Most important, learn to listen to what your client is telling you, both verbal and non-verbal, listen to the 'music' of your conversation and use your intuition, as well as your knowledge.

TIP: Chapter 2 contains more details about the consultation process.

Contra-indications

It is vital that you discover whether the client has any condition that makes it inadvisable to treat them or necessary for you to have permission from their doctor to do so. There could also be localised problems that require you to modify your treatment and conditions that indicate that you cannot use certain oils (see 'unsafe oils and cautions' section and safety data in the individual oil profiles).

TIP: Do not treat your client if they have a fever or infectious illness or are under the influence of alcohol or drugs.

Seek medical approval before treating anyone suffering from a serious condition, cancers, heart disease, very high or low blood pressure, dysfunction of the nervous system or pregnancy.

Do not massage locally:

I over an area with any history of thrombosis or phlebitis

I over severe varicose veins

I over a skin disorder which could be spread

I over bruising, recent scars or cuts, ulcers or boils

I over recent sprains, fractures, surgical procedures

I torn muscles, ligaments or swellings

I over swollen or inflamed areas.

Take particular care in your choice of oils with anyone suffering from epilepsy, high/low blood pressure, diabetes, allergy sufferers or those with a family history of allergy, skin sensitivity or pregnancy.

What form of treatment?

When you have gathered information from the consultation you will need to analyse this data in order to decide what to do. These are some suggestions:

I What is the client's main problem/reason for their visit.

I How severe is it? – the more severe, the more treatments may be needed.

I How long term is it? – with on going problems it is possible to space treatments wider apart.

I What are the subsidiary issues? – this will help you to choose the oils.

I Is it realistic to think that the treatment can be helpful?

I How often and how frequently is the client willing and able to come for treatment?

I What can you offer in the way of homecare between treatments?

Many clients will come for aromatherapy as a treat, possibly a birthday present, but others will have a more specific reason for coming. Some may be experiencing particularly stressful events in their lives while others may have difficulties associated with the menstrual cycle. Some may be suffering from headaches and benefit from a treatment of head, neck or shoulders only, while others may have swollen ankles and benefit from lymphatic drainage of the legs. You may treat clients who are infirm or disabled and are restricted in which parts of their body you can massage. All these aspects need to be taken into consideration as you develop a treatment plan – discuss and agree it with your client. Remember, many people will be reluctant to commit themselves to a course of treatments until they have experienced it and felt the benefits, so be flexible. In the course of the massage you may also discover factors which will make you want to amend your plan.

Which oils?

The next step is to choose some oils for this treatment. There are many different ways to do so, but possibly the most straightforward for beginners is as follows. First rule out any oils which are contra-indicated. Then from the picture of the client you have formed, decide on a central issue and perhaps two or three lesser issues; for example, your client is very tense, and is not sleeping well and suffering occasionally from headaches or stomach pains. Pick out a selection of five or six oils that best address these issues from your knowledge of their properties. Check your client's response to these; this is best done by putting a drop of the oil on a tissue and wafting it under their nose. Discard any that your client dislikes. From those remaining, use your knowledge of blending (next section) to choose three and decide how many drops of each you will mix to create your blend (see later section for how much oil to use). Measure your base oil, usually 10 ml, and pour into a ramekin or similar vessel and add your drops of oil and mix well.

Check this blend with your client by rubbing a little onto the back of their hand and letting them smell it. If they dislike it, it probably will not do them much good and you will unfortunately have to try again until you get a satisfactory blend.

It is possible to use one, two or three oils, but usually not more. Three gives you a wide range of possibilities plus the possibility or synergistic effects. Now you are all set and ready to go!

Figure 10.5 Wafting oil under nose to test

Principles of blending

There are limitless combinations of essential oils possible to create blends. Where does the beginner begin to choose what to put with what?

First, it helps to understand that there are different bases on which to make the decision.

1. Aesthetic – aiming to create a pleasing fragrance. This is akin to what a perfumier does, and is based on an appreciation of the fragrance qualities of the oils.

2. Clinical or medical – aiming to maximise the benefit to health. This is based on a knowledge of the therapeutic benefits of the oils.

In practice, both these bases can be used. It is more pleasing and more beneficial to use a remedy that smells attractive. This is a very subjective individual matter. Although there are some guidelines given below, you will only really learn by experimenting and checking with your clients.

Figure 10.6 Glass ramekin containing oil

Oils can be divided into families depending upon which part(s) of the plant that they come from; for example, florals, spices, herbs, resins, trees, and will generally blend happily with other oils from the same family. There are popular links also; for example, citrus with spice, wood with resin, herb with flower. Oils which share chemical constituents will blend well. Oils which come from the same botanical family will blend well.

Synergy: there are certain oils which are thought to enhance each other's properties and effectiveness, in such a way that 'the whole is greater than the sum of the parts'. You will come across many examples of synergistic blends in text books, based on the author's experience.

Notes

Aromas have been classified by perfumiers like notes on a musical scale. A simplified version is sometimes used by aromatherapists.

I Top notes have a fresh, light quality. They evaporate fast, and are fast acting. They tend to be stimulating and uplifting; for example, lemon, eucalyptus, petitgrain.

I Middle notes provide the heart of a fragrance. They evaporate more slowly, tend to affect the body metabolism; for example, geranium, juniper, lavender.

I Base notes are rich and heavy, they emerge slowly and linger. They tend to be sedating and relaxing; for example, sandalwood, rose and frankincense.

It is sometimes suggested that a blend should contain a balance of notes. Base notes in particular can 'fix' and hold top note oils, but this may be more important in creating perfumes than in making therapeutic blends.

Odour intensity

Some oils smell much stronger than others and will dominate your blends unless you take this into account by using less of them in relation to other oils, also remember that the 'note' gives you guidance as to how quickly the aroma will hit you and how long it will last. Here is a guideline to odour intensity, but remember that we all receive and process scents individually so this may not reflect your own experience:

I high: black pepper, camomile, eucalyptus, frankincense and tea tree

I fairly high: clary sage, geranium and rosemary

I medium: juniper, lavender, lemon, petitgrain and rose absolute

I low: sandalwood.

10ml vegetable oil

Figure 10.7 Pouring oil into a ramekin

Compatibility

Some oils seem to 'fight' and do not become a harmonious blend when mixed, for example rose and eucalyptus, peppermint and orange, while others seem to belong naturally together, for example lavender and camomile.

Do not take everything you read as gospel truth about what will or will not go with what – try it out and form your own opinion – bearing in mind all precautions.

How much essential oil should I use?

Let us start with a rule of thumb, and then look at the factors which might modify it.

The rule is to use 5–6 drops of oil for a massage for an average-sized adult client.

You would decrease this in the following circumstance:

I smaller client – for example a child. Be guided by body weight, e.g.half adult body weight use 2–3 drops.

I frail client

I client with sensitive skin

I pregnant client

I Depending on the aims of the treatment. Some aromatherapists believe that if you are first and foremost attempting to influence the client's emotional state rather than addressing a physical problem it is more effective to use less oil.

I You may decrease if you are treating a smaller area of the body, but not necessarily, as the important consideration is the quantity of essential oil that is penetrating the body.

You may increase the number of drops if you are treating a larger client, but remembering the point above, do not go above 8 drops of essential oil, no matter how much base oil you may need.

Massage blends are often expressed as a percentage dilution. The standard dilution is 2.5–3 per cent, which means 5–6 drops in 10 ml of base oil. It is considered that 20 drops of oil = 1 ml. This is a nominal amount, since size of drops is not standard, thus 10 ml = 200 drops therefore 5–6 in 10 ml = 5–6 in 200 = 2.5–3 per cent.

Base oils

When you are diluting your essential oils to use them in massage, there is a wide choice of base oils available. You must always choose a vegetable oil, obtained from seeds or nut, rather than a mineral oil such as baby oil. This is primarily because mineral oils form a barrier between the skin and the outside: they have relatively large molecules which cannot penetrate the skin and thus would make it hard for the essential oils to enter the body.

Cold pressed or relatively unrefined vegetable oils are the best because they retain the maximum possible amount of proteins, vitamins, essential fatty acids and trace elements from their source, which are nourishing and beneficial for the client. The oils found in supermarket shelves are manufactured by processes involving heat, which destroys the vitamins, etc., or chemical solvents which leave the oils impure.

The most commonly used oils are grapeseed, sweet almond, apricot kernel, sunflower, olive, safflower and soya oils. To these may be added a range of other oils that are more expensive and have some particularly desirable properties; for example, jojoba, evening primrose, avocado, borage seed, macadamia and wheat germ.

You will need to research the particular qualities and uses of these base oils (see further studies section).

APPLYING AROMATHERAPY MASSAGE

Standards of hygiene and personal appearance are identified in chapter 4.

Layout of working space

This, of course, is similar to the requirements for body massage (see chapter 7). Ensure that you can move freely around the couch and that everything you need is to hand. The treatment room should be warm and softly lit and you may be able to play relaxing music during the massage.

You will need:

I a trolley lined with tissue roll

I couch covered with towels or blanket and tissue role, with a face hole if possible

I a variety of warm towels to cover your client

I small towels to use as props where required

I a pillow, if required

I record card, consultation sheet and pen

I surgical spirit or other cleanser

I cotton wool pads or tissues

I selection of essential oils

I measuring equipment

I ramekin or similar for mixed oil

I selection of base oils

I notes on the properties of essential oils

I waste bin.

Client care

Review chapters 7 and 2. In particular ensure that your client understands what the treatment involves. Encourage them to visit the toilet prior to treatment and check with them that they are warm and comfortable on the couch. During the massage check frequently that your pressure is as they like it and look out for non-verbal signs, as well; for example, goose flesh, fidgeting, lifting head, not relaxing and held breath. Not everyone finds it easy to say if they are uncomfortable or do not like something.

The massage sequence

There are as many varieties of aromatherapy massage as there are practising aromatherapists. You will be taught a particular sequence. As you become experienced you will undoubtedly begin to introduce your own variations, bringing in movements that you have learnt elsewhere and subtly altering your strokes. In fact you will probably never give exactly the same massage twice, which is how it should be as you are responding to the individuality of your client.

In general terms aromatherapy massage differs from others forms of massage in that it is gentler and more concerned with a general experience of relaxation and well being than with specific muscle groups. Strong percussive movements and vigorous petrissage are omitted while finger pressures are included. These may be called acupressure or shiatsu pressures while a deeper version is termed neuro muscular massage. You will need to research and practise these techniques (see further study section).

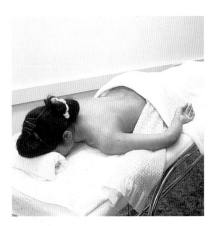

Figure 10.8 Client ready to receive aromatherapy massage

Quality of touch, rhythm and pressure

Whatever sequence you practise, what is of the greatest importance is the quality of your touch, that is, the caring contact that you make with your client through your hands. This will be affected by your own state of mind; if you are tense and preoccupied your client will pick this up at some level, and not benefit fully. You will discover that the massage can provide a period of peace and nourishment for you, as well as for the client.

For the client to float off into a state of perfect relaxation, your rhythm needs to be regular, without sudden starts and stops and loss of contact and your pressure must be appropriate for this client. As you become experienced this will probably become automatic for you, but do check. For some people, a light pressure is irritating or ticklish, or they do not feel that they have been 'met' somehow. For others, a deeper pressure feels heavy, invasive or uncomfortable.

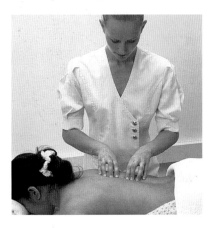

Figure 10.9 Application of finger pressures on back

Variations with different clients

Apart from more subtle variations mentioned above you will probably have to treat many different kinds of clients.

1. Pregnant women. Once you have checked that she has medical approval, be guided by her wishes. You may need to omit the abdomen sequence, but many women will greatly appreciate very gentle slow stroking over the abdomen. If she cannot lie on her front you will have to adapt your sequence. It is possible to massage the back either with her lying on her side, or sitting facing the couch and

leaning on a pillow (see illustration). Remember to use props under the knees and elsewhere as required when she lies on her back.

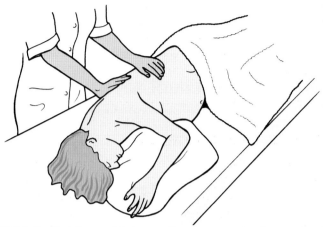

Figure 10.10 Position for receiving aromatherapy massage when pregnant

2. Children. Use less essential oil, less base oil and keep the massage shorter and less formal, with more stress on lighter movements.

3. Male. Generally, a man will require a firmer pressure. You will probably want to omit erogenous zones to save embarrassment. Remember that hairy skin can present a problem of drag. You will need more base oil and may need to work more in the direction of the hair growth. On the face, substitute pressures for effleurage.

4. Injured or infirm. Some people are not able to get up on the couch, and then you will have to use your ingenuity. They can sit in a chair leaning over on the couch or leaning back on you (see illustration) while you massage their head and neck. You can work on legs and feet while they sit and you sit on a low stool at their feet, with their foot propped up on a towel on your lap. There are many other possibilities, but do watch the strain on your own back.

5. Overweight. May require help up onto the couch and a pillow under the breasts when lying on the front. Generally you will need to emphasise those parts of your routine which stimulate the lymphatic system and the break down and flushing out of toxins from the body. You should, of course, have gained some ideas from your consultation about the causes, and will work in line with this. Dietary advice may be helpful but it is probably of no use to someone who is overeating because they are depressed, for example.

When you have finished a treatment allow your client to rest before dressing, then:

| evaluate effectiveness (see next section)
| give homecare advice (see next section)
| revise the record card
| show your client to reception/process the bill/make future appointments
| tidy work area, send towels to laundry, dispose of waste and clean up.

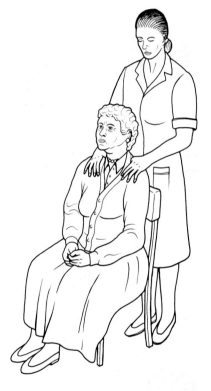

Figure 10.11 Infirm client receiving massage

EVALUATING YOUR TREATMENT

After the treatment you will want to know how effective it was. This will help you to make decisions about future sessions and advice the you give your client for homecare.

163

How does your client look?

Are they asleep, or much more relaxed than when you started? Has the skin tone improved? Are the eyes brighter? Are they breathing more deeply and evenly? Is there more freedom of movement in a joint, less pain in a muscle, or reduced swelling? Does the client seem more alive?

What does your client say?

Clients will usually make spontaneous comments on your treatment, but you will also want to seek detailed feedback. It is good practice for a colleague to administer a short written questionnaire – many people are much too shy or polite to voice any dissatisfactions to the person concerned, but may do so to someone more neutral. Does your salon already have a form? Think about what information would be really useful to you and design one yourself.

Temporary and cumulative effects

Some of the physical effects you can expect are detailed above. Many are temporary, but after a number of sessions you could expect the changes to last for longer after each treatment, and become easier to generate. So each time you cover the old ground and go on a little further. With chronic problems such as migraine or arthritis you may not see dramatic changes. If the client is suffering from stress and does nothing to change their life style, your efforts will offer temporary relief. On the other hand, it could inspire them to make long-term changes and then you will see substantial improvements. Sometimes the differences are very subtle, but you and your client will be aware of a gradually increasing sense of well-being.

Aftercare and homecare

You can give your client advice to support your treatment. First, to get maximum benefit from the massage and the oils:

- avoid bath or shower for 8 hours
- avoid bath oils for 24 hours
- try to drink only water or herbal teas for 24 hours
- avoid sugar – use honey as a substitute
- eat light meals and try to take it easy after the session.

You can suggest that they use certain essential oils at home in their bath, to vaporise or inhale in steam or from tissue, as appropriate (see further study).

These may be the same oils you have used in the massage or you may decide others are more appropriate. You could make up a bath oil or skin cream or a concentrated mix – pure essential oil. If you do the latter, be sure that your client understands, thoroughly, how to use it safely.

SUMMARY

You will appreciate from the context of this chapter the complexity of essential oils and that they may be used in beauty therapy to enhance the client's feeling of well being. As important as the oils used is the atmosphere in which the service is provided. Always pay attention to your client, throughout the process of consultation, provision and evaluation. The findings of the evaluation are used to inform further treatments.

FURTHER STUDY

1. Find out about how essential oils are extracted from plant materials, especially steam and water distillation, solvent extraction and expression.

2. Find out about the types of chemical compounds found in essential oils, terpenes, esters, aldehydes, ketones, alcohols, phenols and oxides. What are the general properties of each group?

3. Find out about how to administer patch tests for allergic reactions or sensitivity to essential oils. Check which oils are particularly recommended for pregnant women and nursing mothers.

4. Research some other useful oils; for example, bergamot, cypress, grapefruit, marjoram, patchouli, peppermint, thyme and ylang ylang.

5. Look in a range of aromatherapy books for examples of synergistic blends and take note of those suggested by two or more, then try them out.

6. Find out about the properties and particular uses of a range of vegetable oils.

7. Research the movements and effects of finger pressures and neuromuscular massage.

8. Find out how to use the essential oils in the bath, in steam inhalations, on compresses and in vaporisers. What particular safety precautions would you take for each? How many drops of oil would you use for each?

9. Refresh your memory of anatomy and physiology. You need an understanding of all the systems of the body, the skin, muscles, bones, joints, circulation, lymphatic, nervous, respiratory, digestive, renal, endocrine and immune and how they can be affected by massage.

10. Find out about the history of aromatherapy and the use of essential oils for medical purposes in ancient civilisations.

Review questions

1. What are essential oils?

2. How does the molecular size of a vegetable oil differ from that of mineral oil?

3. In what type of container should essential oil be stored?

4. What precaution should be taken before providing aromatherapy massage to a client who is at present undertaking homeopathic medication?

5. List five 'families' of oils.

6. What is 'synergy'?

7. How many drops of essential oil would you add to a 10 ml volume to create a 5 per cent solution?

8. How would you adjust your treatment when providing aromatherapy massage to children?

9. What is meant by the term 'odour intensity'?

10. How soon following aromatherapy massage may your client bath or shower?

11

Specialist make up

Clients requiring corrective make up may have a range of complex issues that the therapist must cope with and positively respond to. This chapter will provide guidance in some of those issues and how to approach them. It will also introduce you to a range of techniques for both covering disfigurement as well as correcting appearance.

Elements

18.1 Assess clients and prepare treatment plans

18.2 Prepare the work area and client for the application of make up

18.3 Apply make up using specialist techniques

18.4 Advise on self application and aftercare

CONTENTS

Introduction	167
Patients and consultation	167
Treatment plan	168
Treatment work area	169
Your camouflage kit	170
Camouflage technique	170
Colour matching	171
Application for scars, bruises and skin marks	171
Application for tattoos	172
Application for leg veins	173
Corrective technique	173
Eyes	173
Nose	174
Face shape	175
Lip	176
Prosthetics	176
Postiche	177
Aftercare	178
Summary	178
Further study	178
Review questions	179

Con
Obje
Trea
Add
Trea
Clie
Can
Date

The tre
up – oft
and cor
patient'
records
disfigur
of the t
(measu
be judg
out. Th
manufa
step ap
referen
their ov
   Kno
Contra
Disc
Sen
Wan
Ope
Rais

Specific
reaction
cause s
   Take
technic
unders
   The
and no
You sho
rules an

TRE

You ma
service
provide
a work
meets l
may va
is prov
beauty
organis
   You
under

INTRODUCTION

Perceived or actual bodily disfigurement and non-desirable features of the body's appearance may, in certain circumstances, destroy your client's self-confidence and self esteem. As the therapist you will need to equip yourself with the necessary skills to educate your client in how best to camouflage or correct these so called disfigurements, enabling them to regain their self-confidence.

As inferred earlier, disfigurement may be actual or may be a perception that your client has of a normal bodily appearance. For example, you client may have scarring or skin blemish that is located on an area of the body which is not covered by clothing, this disfigurement is not a usual feature of a person's appearance and will often cause distress to them both because of the effect on their appearance and the apparent effect that this has on others. For some clients a normal bodily shape, for example a broad nose can cause distress and while it may not normally be termed a disfigurement; for that client it can be a major distressing factor. A corrective make up will reduce the appearance of these features.

As a camouflage therapist your consultations may take place within a clinical environment such as: a department of a hospital that specialises with bodily disfigurements caused in a variety of ways; a clinic specialising in particular causes of disfigurement, for example burns or; you may provide the service within a beauty therapy salon. You may have developed a good reputation for your skills in this area and you may find that medical practitioners refer patients to you. You may also be providing this service as part of a photographic, film/video or television environment covering skin blemishes of models and artists as a one off prior to 'shooting'.

PATIENTS AND CONSULTATION

You should consider your clients as patients as they will often come to you with a range of complex physiological problems linked to the condition that you are to camouflage. Your consultation should be undertaken in a private area where your patient's confidentiality can be maintained. This is of particular relevance if you wish your client to disclose information or to expose areas of the body.

Start your consultation by listening – do not presume that you already know what your patient's needs are. To presume and subsequently project this assumption onto your patient may result in failure to understand their needs fully. Without a full awareness there is a risk that you may treat only part of the problem and not fulfill your patient's expectations. When working with an insecure person there is a risk that, by projecting your perceptions of their problem, you may raise issues that were not previously a problem for them. So listen to your patient. Have patience as it may take time for your patient to become confident in discussing and disclosing their problems. Use tact and take care to react in a professional manner. Remember that, as a camouflage therapist you will see and handle bodily features that may often be quite distressing and that by flinching or showing revulsion may be very distressing to a patient who may at that moment be undergoing considerable mental anguish in exposing themselves to you.

When you are providing a consultation for a patient who has an unknown condition or one that you suspect as being contagious you should refer them to a general practitioner (GP). You may otherwise find that you are camouflaging the symptoms of a disorder that may

TIP: If you suspect your patient to be contra-indicated to the treatment check with their GP before proceeding.

with Tungsten filament light bulbs cause blue and green shades to appear darker and red shades to appear brighter than in daylight. White fluorescent light tubes cause blue and green pigments to look brighter and red shades darker. Warm white fluorescent light tubes give a light similar to daylight. Remember that photographic light may cause differing colour effects and may also detect differing reflective properties of make up. As you will most often be educating and instructing your patient in self-application you will often require a lit mirror so that your client may track the application procedure.

You should always have an adequate supply of sterilised equipment or sterilising equipment – information about sterlisation is provided in the chapter 4 – Working Safely. There must be adequate facility to wash and sanitise your hands throughout the consultation and treatment.

Guidance in professional appearance and dress codes is provided within chapter 4 – Working Safely.

Your camouflage kit

Your make up kit may be best contained within an easily cleaned toolbox. This will enable you to travel with this to a variety of locations to work. Your kit will contain small amounts of the following:

I Antiseptic
I Cleansing preparations
I Cotton wool
I Tissues
I Range of camouflage creams
I Range of make up
I Samples of cover creams
I False eyelash kit
I Spirit gun
I Double sided adhesive patches
I Applicator, sponges and brushes
I Fixing powder
I Spatulas
I Orange sticks
I Mirror
I Scissors
I Soap
I Sterile water
I Note pad/pen/record cards

You should maintain a supply of sample sized camouflaging make up so that your patient may take away with them a supply of cosmetics for immediate use. Having trained your client in correct application procedures they may be keen to practice this and to maintain the continuity of their look.

CAMOUFLAGE TECHNIQUE

Camouflage techniques focus upon covering or masking undesirable disfigurement, including scars, birthmarks and/or leg veins. Camouflage make-up may last for several days though it is recommended that facial camouflage is removed daily; as otherwise dirt and natural perspiration may block the skin's pores. Some patients will prefer to retain the effect for longer periods on other areas of the body, others may elect to remove it and reapply at more frequent intervals. The sensitivity of your patient's skin may be an influencing factor. While most cover creams will be waterproof; soap will loosen cream and may produce a patchy effect. Avoid rubbing the treated area after bathing, blotting dry is preferable to avoid smudging. Climate will have an effect on the longevity of the camouflage, in warmer climates the perspiration will more rapidly loosen the cream.

Creams may be effectively removed using cream cleansers

TIP: Those living in hot climates may need to reapply cream more than once a day. This is because they are likely to get a build up of perspiration and oils which will effect the cover cream's stability.

Colour matching

For effective camouflage it is important to select cover creams which match the colour of the surrounding skin. Within the container cover creams will often appear a different colour than when applied to the patient's skin. This difference may be the result of:

 - chemical reaction between acidity of the skin and the cream
 - influence by the skin's colour through the cover cream.

Test the effect of cover cream by applying a sample to part of the area to be covered. To make efficient use of the test try two or more shades at one time to determine the best match. Often a perfect match will not be available and shades will have to be mixed together in order for the camouflage to be effective. You will need to devise a measure that can be effective and accurate for the small amounts of product that you will be measuring for the test. Keep a record of the shades and proportions mixed so that they may be reproduced effectively in the future.

Differing makes of cover cream may have varying coverage effects and should be tested to find that most appropriate to your patient's needs. You should make yourself familiar with differing ranges of products so that you can select and advice effectively.

Application for scars, bruises and skin marks

As you gain experience you will adapt and develop techniques of application that are effective and suit your style of work. These are some basic rules of good practice:

 - Gown your patient to protect their clothing
 - Using a clean headband secure your patient's hair back off the face (if working on an area onto which the hair is likely to fall)
 - Prepare you work station and ensure that adequate supplies of materials are available
 - Thoroughly cleanse and sanitise your hands
 - Explain the treatment fully to your client
 - Before any cover cream is applied, cleanse the area to be treated. Dirt or grease can cause the make up to 'slide'
 - Apply the selected cover cream sparingly. Cover cream should be applied only to the area of disfigurement, avoid allowing this to be applied to unaffected areas. This will maintain a more natural look and the cream will be less likely to rub off onto your patient's cloths. Apply a second or third coat having set the previous coat using a setting powder. These additional coats may be applied to all of the treatment

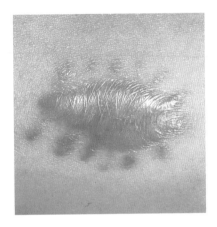

Figure 11.1 Keloid scar

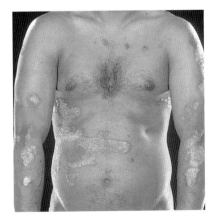

Figure 11.2 Psoriasis

171

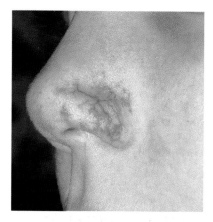

Figure 11.3 Capillary naevus

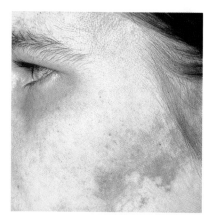

Figure 11.4 Port wine stain or cutaneous naevus

💬TIP: Remember, your patient will need instruction on how to apply the camouflage. Provide step by step instruction as you work.💬

💬TIP: Your patient may require more than one lesson in how to apply the camouflage. For patient satisfaction ensure that they are able to undertake the application effectively.💬

area or selectively to just those areas where the disfigurement is still visible.

Do not set the previous coat when blending differing cover creams to produce a particular colour effect, an example would be when blending red onto the cheek area. You may apply cover cream in a range of ways:

Brush – a fine brush to apply cream to a thin scar or disfigurement. Apply the cream to the scar area only and then using a finger tap the scar to blend the edge into the skin.

Sponge – a damp cosmetic sponge may be used to provide a light covering. This method can be effective in covering light bruising of the skin. The moistened sponge is applied to an amount of cover cream that has akeady been removed from its container (to prevent cross-infection) and then applied by gently pressing to the skin. Before applying to the disfigurement test on the back of your hand to avoid overload.

Finger – cream may be applied using the finger. Large areas may be covered using rubbing movement. Ensure that only the area of disfigurement is covered.

Ⅰ Apply setting powder from a dry piece of cotton wool to the cover cream having allowed it to dry (approximately 10 minutes). Apply a liberal coating ensuring that you do not miss any area where you have placed the cream. Lightly brush off excess powder using downward strokes of a soft brush or cotton wool. Finally lightly blot the area with damp cotton wool, this will remove any powdery fill and help to set the camouflage.

Indented (atrophic) and protruding (hypertrophic) scars

Light and shade may be used to reduce the contoured appearance of these forms of scaring In the case of indented scars apply a lighter shade around the inside edge of the scar, as the skin indents, around the outside of the indent apply a slightly darker cream just around the outside of the indent. Blend both to the skin by tapping lightly with the finger. For protruding scars the opposite may be used; applying a slightly darker shade to the inside edge of the scar and a slightly lighter shade to the skin just outside the edge of the scar, blending by tapping.

The results may be variable, being more effective in some cases than others.

Keloid scars

Due to the nature of the scaring – see illustration – it is difficult to effectively camouflage this. Cover cream may be applied by a finger application followed by a second application, by brush, on the raised puckered areas. The effect achieved will hide the discoloration but not reduce the appearance of the contours.

Application for tattoos

This type of skin marking may be difficult to camouflage.

Ⅰ Apply a first coat of cover cream using a brush to carefully paint over the dyes of the tattoo. Use shades which match the skin. You may consider tones which will neautralise the pigments, therefore olive or green over red or orange over blue.

Application for leg veins

This can be quite an intricate process to carefully apply, using a fine brush, each vein. The tone used will usually be within the olive range. Once this has been set, a skin matching shade should be applied using a fine brush. This application may be blended by finger tapping, set and blotted.

CORRECTIVE TECHNIQUE

Corrective techniques focus upon altering the apparent form of a bodily feature, including face shape, nose shape, lip shape or size and/or eye shape or size. The technique is mainly that of using light and shade to draw the observer's attention to particular features while allowing other features to withdraw into the background

The ideal face shape is said to be an oval. Being balanced and with no obvious irregularities this fits with the current perceptions of normality and good looks. You will need to identify the shape of your patient's face to understand some of their associated features and to build on the positives while minimising those features that are less desirable.

Within this field you may be called upon to reduce the irregular facial shapes often caused through strokes, accidents and/or surgery and will need to draw upon your knowledge of the effects of light and shade as well as facial characteristics.

You will need colors including white or light colours that reflect light easily, this will make the areas upon which this is used more prominent. Colours that do not reflect light may be used as shaders and will produce the effect of depth and hollowness. These may be brown, deep blue and dark grey.

Eyes

Small eyes can be given width by highlighting around the outer corners.

Prominent projecting eyes with over hanging eyebrows. Dark shades on the eye-lid and above. The highlighter used above blending all together where they meet.

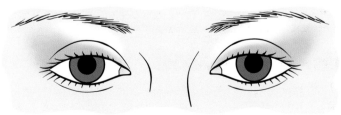

TIP: Remember that the colour and tone of our skin varies throughout the year; for example, if your client takes a holiday that involves exposure to UV light, the yellow tones may be more apparent in the skin.

TIP: Explain to your client the appropriate procedure for the removal of cover cream.

Drooping eyes. Highlight the area above the eyes using shader on the outside corners.

Nose

Broad nose

Applying shader in parallel lines either side of the nose to the eyebrows may correct the apparent width of the nose. The line of shade is placed parallel to provide a narrow but even channel to remain un-shaded. The further down the nose that the line of shade is extended the longer the nose will appear

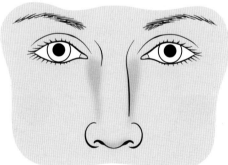

Long nose

A long nose shape may be corrected by the application of shader to the very tip of the nose as well as the application of shader either side of the nose up to the corner of the eyes.

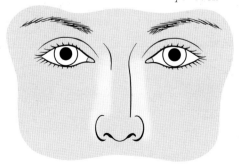

Thin nose

Apply highlighter to either side of the nose to eye level.

Bent nose

Apply shader in parallel lines either side of the nose. Leave a straight line of non-shade down the middle.

Bulbous nose end

Apply shader to either side of the bulbous area of the nose.

Face shape

Blusher can be applied to correct the contours and draw the observer's eyes to colour rather thin shape. Shader may also be used to take to the background areas away, including comers of chin from square of pear shapes. The application of shade must be subtle to avoid drawing the observer's attention to the corrective action.

Square   **Round**

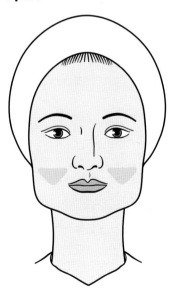 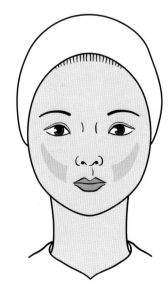

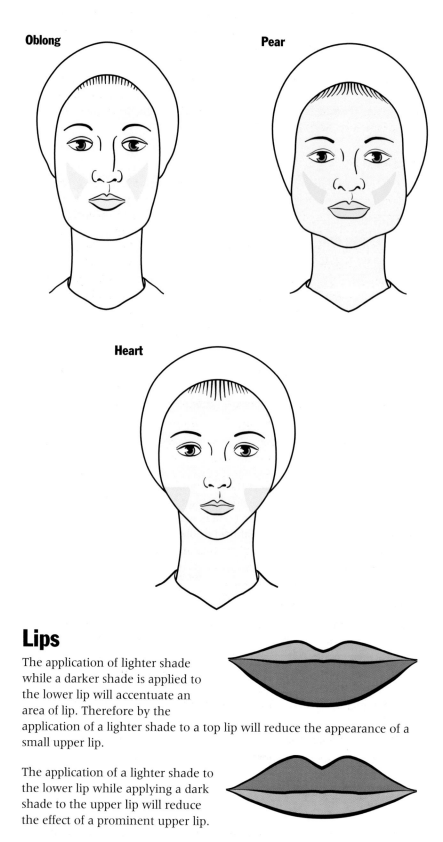

Oblong **Pear**

Heart

Lips

The application of lighter shade while a darker shade is applied to the lower lip will accentuate an area of lip. Therefore by the application of a lighter shade to a top lip will reduce the appearance of a small upper lip.

The application of a lighter shade to the lower lip while applying a dark shade to the upper lip will reduce the effect of a prominent upper lip.

Prosthetics

These manufactured artificial appendages are designed to simulate the appearance, and often the function, of living tissue. This improves the patient's quality of life by providing them with an appearance closer to accepted norms. Examples are artificial limbs, eyes, ears, nose etc. Occasionally you may be employed to camouflage an area of inflammation near the edge of the prosthetic. This may take the form of blending a join and colour difference. Specialist make up is available for the application to certain surfaces of prosthetics. This make up is often grease based to attach itself to latex surfaces.

Postiche

Wigs or postiche are made either human or synthetic hair. The human hair wig may be manufactured to fit the wearer, increasingly synthetic mass produced wigs are provided which will fit a range of head shapes and sizes. Hand made wigs can be costly due to the labour intensive nature of the manufacture. Machine made wigs, usually made in the Far East, can have a very natural appeaunce while being made to fit a range of head shapes and sizes. Due to the lower cost of machine made postiche the National Health Service currently favors it. Eyebrows and eyelashes may be beneficial for the concealment of damage brought about by scarring, where no hair growth can subsequently take place.

> **TIP:** Retail products should be available so that your client may immediately maintain the treatment without having to visit other suppliers.

Fitting postiche

The term postiche is given to any form of added hair work. A full wig is often the most effective means of coverage of hair loss on scalp areas. The wig may easily be fitted by the wearer themselves. Method of placement:

l Secure any of the wearer's own hair within the hairline area.

l Locate a specialised net cap to secure the wearer's hair and provide a fixing/attachment point for the wig.

l Insert your hands inside the wig foundation to open it.

l Locate the front hairline in place and then ease the wig over the scalp area.

l Ensure all of the wearers own hair is tucked within the net cap.

l Ensure a secure fit of the wig by adjusting any tension springs, often located at the nape of the wig.

l Pins or grips may be used to secure.

l Dress the hair into place.

For a more natural front hairline, particularly when the hairline is exposed, a fine net base known as 'hair lace' may be used. This very fine net base once made of woven human hair is now made of very fine synthetic fibre and can appear invisible when placed on the skin. It must be attached to the skin using spirit gum and then a light application of make up applied to blend. In order to fix the 'hair lace' follow this procedure:

> **TIP:** Your patient may need several sessions to learn how to most effectively fix postiche in place.

l Cleanse the skin's surface onto which the hair lace is to be attached.

l Apply a thin application of spirit gum to the contact area

l Allow to slightly set.

l Apply the postiche locating the hair lace first

l Locate all of the postiche.

l Using a moist chamois leather blot the surface of the net where it is attached to the gum This can help to firm and flatten the net as well as reducing any shine produced by the gum.

l Lightly blend with make up.

TIP: Spirit gum and its solvent can be inflammable, do not use near naked flame or in restricted areas.

Build up of spirit gum may be removed from the hair lace by the use of a solvent, often surgical spirit. Small hard or solid based hairpieces, such as toupees are often secured in place using specialised double sided adhesive tape. These patches are secured to specially strengthened and protected areas of the foundation. To attached to the head:

I Attach the double sided adhesive tape to the underside of the postiche.

I Cleanse the area of the scalp to which the adhesive is tobe attached. Remove any hair from these areas of the scalp.

I Remove the protective layer from the second surface of the double sided adhesive tape.

I Locate the postiche in place starting at the front hairline

I Press firmly to the scalp

AFTERCARE

Your patients will usually wish to maintain their new appearance following their visit to you. You should maintain a supply of products and materials that you use so that your patient may be equipped to maintain the look without delay and difficulty.

It is often best to maintain a supply of products of small unit sizes. This can reduce the overhead of large volumes of stock being held and enable a wider range to be maintained.

Provide your patient with a written plan for the application of their make up. Provide sufficient guidance in the effective application of their make up. The level of guidance required will vary between patients. Use each treatment meeting as an opportunity to provide guidance and instruction in self-application. Be honest with your patient about their ability to maintain their new look.

Remember that the skin's colouration may change during the year due to exposure to sunlight as well as with aging and therefore regular check should be arranged to maintain the effectiveness of the cover.

If your client is referred by a general practitioner they may be able to obtain the relevant products through prescription.

TIP: As a basic rule when selecting a suitable shade of cover cream, always look for the underlying colour in the skin.

TIP: You will achieve a more natural result if you apply several thin coats setting each separately, rather than one thick coat.

SUMMARY

On the surface, the provision of remedial camouflage make-up may appear to be purely an outward covering service. However, through the content of this chapter you will appreciate that the service can give a considerable level of psychological relief for your patient who owns the disfigurement. As important as the make-up is the style in which the service is provided and always builds your patient's self-confidence.

FURTHER STUDY

1. To enable you to appreciate better the psychological effects of disfigurement, debate the pressure that our society can place on an individual who has a disfiguring birth mark.

2. Create a guide to the range of conditions that you may be required to treat, their characteristics and how they may be camouflaged. These should include:

I types of scaring

I dark birthmarks

l Rosacea.

Include details of how these conditions would be camouflaged on the following ethnic characteristics:

l Afro-Caribbean

l Oriental

l Asian

l Caucasian.

Review questions

1. What is the basic rule when selecting an appropriate shade of cream?
2. What is the disadvantage of applying a single thick application of camouflage cream?
3. What information is required by the client following their camouflage treatment?
4. What tool would you use when masking a hairline scar?
5. How do you reduce the shine from spirit gum when attaching hair lace?
6. What effect does shade have upon the appearance of the skin's contours?
7. What is a prosthetic?
8. State 5 contraindications to the application of camouflage.
9. Name three techniques for applying cover cream.
10. How may small eyes be given width?

12 Artifical nail techniques

This chapter will provide you with knowledge and techniques related to changing and maintaining the appearance of nails. You will also be able to assess the suitability of the nails for application and choose the most appropriate product, identify problem situations and know how to remedy some of these. This chapter will also refresh your knowledge with the basics of anatomy and physiology of the nail.

Unit 19

19.1 Assess clients and prepare treatment plans

19.2 Prepare the work area and client for the application of artificial nail structures

19.3 Apply artificial nail structures to meet client requirements

19.4 Maintain artificial nail structures

CONTENTS

Introduction	181
Anatomy and Physiology Review	181
Disorders and diseases of the nail	184
Introduction to nail Extensions	186
Tips and overlay	187
Acrylic	188
Fibre glass	191
Gel	194
Aftercare	196
Summary	196
Further Study	196
Review questions	197

INTRODUCTION

You will find that nail treatments are one of the most satisfying treatments to give to a client as they achieve instant results and therefore instant client satisfaction. Your average client will attend on a regular basis about every four weeks for a full manicure and as often as they like for a re-varnish.

Hands and feet rarely receive the attention that they deserve and a professional manicure will leave them soft and the nails smooth and even, together with a great improvement in their overall presentation.

> **TIP:** Remember you will need to educate your client in the appropriate homecare measures in order to maintain improvement.

ANATOMY AND PHYSIOLOGY

Anatomy and physiology of the hand and forearm

There are 2 bones in the forearm called the radius and ulna that make a moveable joint at the elbow with the humerus bone. There is another moveable joint found at the wrist where the carpals (small wrist joint) joins the forearm. Hinge joints can be found in the fingers; these joints allow flexion (bending) and extension (straightening).

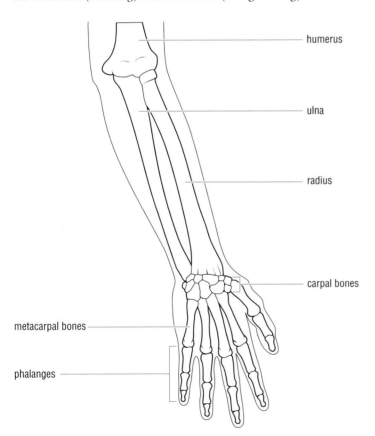

Figure 12.1 Bones of the hand and forearm

The hand and wrist contain 27 bones and out of these 8 are carpals, 5 are metacarpals (long bones at the back of the hand) and 14 are phalanges (fingers) – 2 in the thumb and 3 in each finger, see Figure 7.1.

Anatomy and physiology of lower leg and foot

The lower leg consists of 2 main bones: the tibia (the shin bone) and fibula. They meet with the ankle joint at the talus.

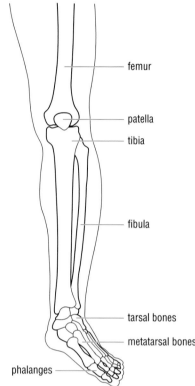

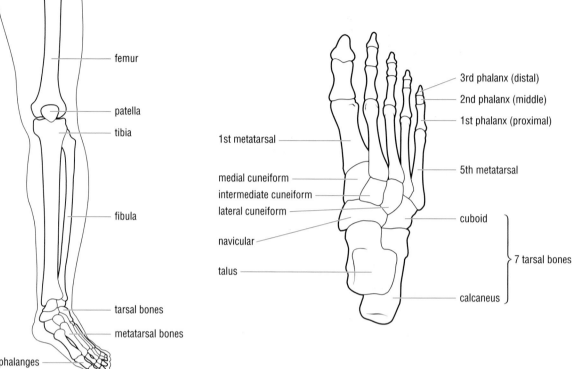

Figure 12.2 Top view and side view of the lower leg

The ankle and foot are made up of 26 bones, in all: 7 tarsals (ankle), 5 metatarsals (forming the length of the foot) and 14 phalanges (toes) – 2 in the big toe and 3 in each of the other toes.

Structure and growth of the nail

Nails are found at the end of each finger and toe. The nail plate is composed of almost clear, compact flat cells containing keratin (hardened protein, also found in hair and skin). These cells are held together with fat and moisture.

The finger nail takes about five months to replace itself and the toe nails 12–18 months.

Functions of the nail

ı To assist with manipulation, i.e. picking up objects, unfastening clasps on jewellery, scratching, etc.

ı To serve as protection for the finger tip and nail bed.

ı To improve your sense of touch.

ı For shock absorption for the protection of bones of the fingers and toes.

TIP: Nail growth can be affected by the condition of the client's health. The normal rate of growth is 3–5 mm per month.

TIP: Keratinisation is the process of the transition of soft to hardened cells by the addition of keratin.

Structure of the nail

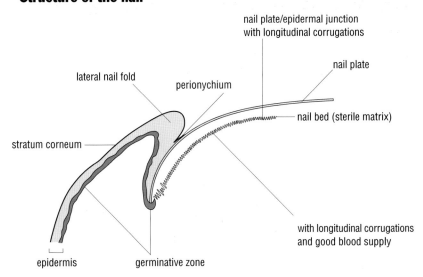

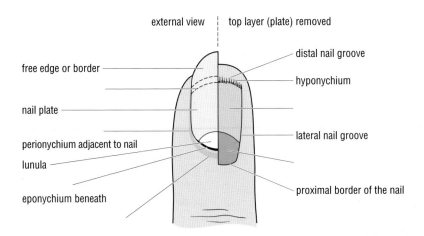

Figure 12.3 Longitudinal cross section of nail showing exposed / unexposed nail plate

- Nail plate – body of the nail which ends at the tip of the fingers and toes and is made of hardened compact tissue. The plate is transparent and acquires its pink colour from the blood supply underneath in the nail bed.
- Free edge – refers to the point of the nail plate that protrudes beyond the finger tip.
- Nail bed – found under the nail plate, the bed is home to a large supply of blood vessels and nerve endings.
- Matrix – living part of the nail from which it grows.
- Root – base of the nail that is surrounded by the nail fold.
- Walls – portion of skin surrounding the nail.
- Grooves – where the edges of the nail plate meet the nail walls.
- Cuticle – growth of skin classified according to its location:
  - Eponychium – cuticle that grows closest to the base of the nail.
  - Perionychium – cuticle which outlines the nail plate.
  - Hyponychium – cuticle found under the free edge.

TIP: The nail can be cut without causing pain but remember that under the nail are many nerve endings which are sensitive to touch and pain.

DISORDERS AND DISEASES OF THE NAIL

Disorder/Disease	Cause	Characteristics	
Atrophy onychatropia	Disorder affecting the matrix to such an extent that reproduction of cells ceases. Do not manicure.	Wasting away of the nail plate.	
Beaus Lines	Disorder caused by a severe illness that effects the function of the matrix.	Horizontal lines across the nail plate.	
Blue nails	Nail condition caused by poor circulation, thought to be linked to a heart disorder.	Discoloured nail plate.	
Dystrophy	Traumatic disorder which affects the matrix. Results are permanent.	Irregular growth of the nail plate. Vertical ridges.	
Eczema	Skin condition. Hereditary factors linked to allergy and stress.	Pi tting of nail plate, furrows present.	
Eggshell nails	Caused by a chronic illness of systemic or nervous origin.	Thin, white nail plate accompanied by unnatural curvature of the nail plate.	
Felon	Infectious and inflamed skin condition caused by incorrect care of hands.	Inflammation, often accompanied by fungal infection.	
Hangnails	Nail condition caused by dehydration of cuticle.	Splitting of the cuticle, leaving it loose.	
Hypertrophy onychauxis	Local infection or bodily disturbance.	Overgrowth of nails, in length or thickness.	
Ingrowing nail Onychocryptosis	Hereditary disorder caused by either poorly fitting shoes or incorrect cutting of the nails.	Often found on toe nails, the sides of the nail grow in to the bed.	
Laddering	Disorder caused by a damaged matrix.	Horizontal ridges.	
Leconychia	Condition due to a minor injury to the nail.	White marks on the nail plate. Very common.	

Disorder/Disease	Cause	Characteristics	
Nail biting Onychophagy	Treatable condition, caused by the individual's nervous disposition.	Biting and chewing the free edge and often exposing the nail bed. Underneath is left a nail weak and rough.	
Onycholysis	Disorder caused by poorly fitting shoes and inappropriate care of the feet.	Nail plate lifts up from the nail bed. The space attracts debris and moisture hence bacterial infection.	
Onychorrhexis, split or brittle nails	Injury or careless maintenance of the hands and nails. Excessive use of chemicals, strong alkalis.	Extreme dryness associated to splitting of the free edge.	
Paronychia	Bacterial infection entering through a crack in the nail fold.	Pus, redness, inflammation and sore.	
Psoriasis	Non-contagious disorder, thought to be hereditary or possibly linked to a nervous disposition.	Small pitting marks on the nail plate, may also affect the skin.	
Pteryguim	Treatable nail condition, caused by overgrowth of the cuticle.	Cuticle adheres to the nail plate at the nail's base growing forward with the nail.	
Ringworm (Tinea Unguiem)	Fungal infection under the free edge. Highly contagious.	Brittle coarse nail plate. The layers of the nail may separate. Discoloration, red rings occurring in patches on the skin.	
Splinter Haemorrhage	A minor trauma.	Streaks places lengthways under the nail plate.	
Spoon-shaped nails Koilonc /chia	Lack of iron in diet, lack of lipids in the nail or congenital.	The nail plate grows into a thin spoon shape.	
Verruca Vulgaris (Common wart)	Viral infection.	A wart that grows inwards on the side of the foot.	
Warts	A viral infection, highly contagious.	Raised growth may be dark or skin may be coloured. May be singular or in clusters.	
Whitlow	Condition affecting the folds of skin around the nail, rendering the nail susceptible to infection.	Throbbing pain. Inflammation, redness, discomfort. If sever, pus may be present.	

Applying acrylic tip and overlay

Liquid and powder acrylic can be used in two ways to produce strong, natural nail extensions: they can be sculpted over a nail form, or they can be sculpted over a tip. The method used is determined by your client's needs. The powders come in four different colours, clear, pink, white and natural, so that different looks can be achieved. Using two colours is a more advanced technique and takes time to master.

With nail tips

I Application takes longer as time is needed to apply the tips, although French tips do not require blending.

I Less sculpting is required as the tip provides the basis of a natural shape and length.

I This method is more expensive but easier, due to the use of tips.

I Less filing is required because the nail is thinner as sculpting is minimal.

With nail forms

I Once the application has been mastered, sculpting over a form is quicker as blending tips is not necessary.

I It is cheaper as no tips are required.

I It is the most difficult technique to learn.

I Should the nail form be incorrectly applied or moved during application, the nail shape is hard to achieve without extensive filing.

ACRYLIC NAILS

Application: nail tips with acrylic overlay

Approximate application time 1 hour to 1½ hours.

1. Wash your hands and ask your client to wash theirs.
2. Remove any varnish and check for any contra-indications (see section 'Disorders and diseases of the nail').
3. Sterilise the nail plate.
4. Push back the cuticles and trim if necessary. This is to ensure that as much nail plate as possible is exposed to allow maximum adhesion to the nail extension.
5. Lightly buff the nail surface to remove shine. Surface oils left on the nail plate will cause lifting. Use a fine grit board or buffer.
6. Select the required tip, which will be determined by the required look, then check tip sizes working from left to right.

Figure 12.6 Nail extension with former

TIP: Acrylic nails, when balanced, are very strong and durable, and are ideal for clients who are rough with their hands or just heavy handed.

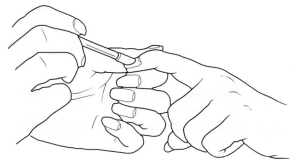

Figure 12.7 Applying primer to nail plate

7. Apply primer to the nail plate and allow to dry.

Figure 12.8 Applying adhesive to tip

> **TIP: Do not allow the primer to touch the cuticle or the nail walls as it is a skin irritant and could cause client discomfort.**

8. Apply a small drop of adhesive (thin tip glue) into the well of the tip.

Figure 12.9 Applying tip

9. Apply the tip at 45° angle to the natural nail. Hold the edge with the well against the free edge, then gently press down and rock the tip, squeezing out all the air bubbles until the tip is flat against the nail surface. If air bubbles appear or if the nail tip is not straight then remove immediately before the adhesive starts to set.

10. Apply a small amount of adhesive to the seam area and allow this to set. This is to ensure that the edge of the tip is securely sealed.

11. Blend the seam area. Begin with a coarse grit file to reduce the bulk.

12. Cut the tip to the desired length.

13. Apply primer to the natural nail only.

14. Dip the brush in liquid, then in clear powder to form a ball the size of a pea. Smooth the acrylic by patting to the side and stroking using the belly of the brush towards the free edge.

15. Dip the brush in the liquid, then in the powder, as before, and apply to the middle of the nail plate. Repeat as before.

16. Dip the brush in liquid, then in powder and apply near the cuticle. This should be a wetter, thinner application to avoid ridges.

17. Visually check the nail from all angles to ensure that the shape is natural.

ABINGDON COLLEGE
LEARNING CENTRE

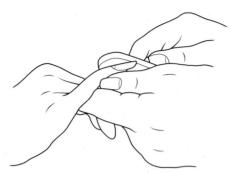

Figure 12.10 Using coarse grit file on hardened nail

18. Once the product has set hard, remove any surface irregularities using a coarse grit file.

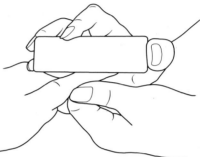

Figure 12.11 Using block buffer

19. Buff the surface to a shine using a block buffer and a three-way shiner.
20. Apply cuticle oil to the skin around the nail.
21. Wash your hands and request your client to wash theirs to remove dust and oil.
22. Apply nail enamel if desired.

Maintenance: acrylic nail extensions

Maintenance should be carried out approximately every two weeks after the initial application. This keeps the nails strong, balanced and attractive.

1. Wash your hands and ask your client to wash theirs. Refer to your client's record card for details of previous nail extension applications.
2. Remove any nail enamel with acetone-free nail enamel remover and check for signs of infection or contra-indication.
3. Push back the cuticle with an orange stick.
4. Buff the seam area with a medium grit file to remove any loose or lifting acrylic. File until the seam becomes invisible. Buff the whole nail plate to remove shine.
5. Remove shine from the re-growth area and apply primer to this area only.
6. Apply a small bead of clear or pink powder near the cuticle. This should be a thin application. Blend in new application by brushing the acrylic down towards the free edge. To prevent sticking, dip the brush into the liquid and wipe clean on a tissue regularly throughout the application.
7. When the acrylic has set hard, smooth the nail surface with a fine grit file.
8. Buff to shine using a buffing block and three-way shine.
9. Apply buffing oil.

10. Both of you should now wash your hands to remove dust and oil.

11. Enamel as usual.

Repairs to acrylic nails

Due to the strength of well balanced acrylic nails, repairs are seldom necessary. If nails are cracked, chipped or broken repairs may be carried out.

Lifting or cracking of the product around the cuticle area

Repair using the maintenance procedure.

Chip or crack in the free edge

1. Use the edge of the file to scuff and widen the crack.

2. You may have to use a nail form to 'fill in' the crack or chip. Wet the old acrylic with liquid to improve adhesions and with new matching coloured acrylic repair the damage.

3. File and buff as in original application.

Free edge broken off

Remove nail extension and replace with a new nail.

Problem solving

▌ Acrylic overlay lifting:
  – incorrect preparation of the natural nail
  – too much or too little product
  – product touching the skin.

▌ Obvious infills:
  – ensure thorough blending in before applying new acrylic.

▌ Nails breaking at the flesh line:
  – not enough product on this area
  – over buffed.

▌ Acrylic crystallizes:
  – room temperature is too cold.

▌ Nails are pointing upwards or downwards:
  – incorrect application of tip
  – check application.

▌ Arch of the nail is irregular:
  – uneven application
  – too much product at sides or middle
  – product too wet causing it to run.

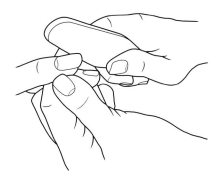

Figure 12.12 Filing a crack

Nail pointing up

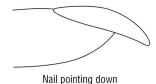

Nail pointing down

Figure 12.13 Nail pointing up and down

FIBREGLASS NAILS

Applying fibreglass nail extensions

Approximate application time 1 hour to 1½ hours.

The finished nail is transparent over the nail bed, allowing the natural pink colour to show through. The nails are very thin and flexible, similar to natural nails. Because the wraps are thin they are ideal to use as a coating over a natural nail for strength or as a repair to a split nail plate.

Fibreglass nails are the least damaging to the natural nails as no primer is needed during application to dehydrate the nail's surface. They are not

TIP: Applications may vary according to manufacturer's guidelines.

suitable for clients with very little nail plate as there has to be sufficient nail plate for the product to adhere to in order to give shape and durability.

The traditional method of fibreglass is using a spray activator, but more modern methods use a brush-on activator and brush-on glue for more control and less fumes. Both are equally strong and selection is based upon the user's preference.

Spray activator application

1. Sanitise your hands and those of your client. Push back the cuticle from the nail plate to allow maximum adhesion.

2. Lightly buff the nail surface to remove shine and surface oils. Use a fine grit board or buffer.

3. Apply a thin coat of resin to the nail plate.

4. Spray with activator. The activator is used to speed up the drying time of the resin and seals the surface to make it non-porous. Depress the pump to check that an even mist of activator is released and spray at least 30 cm away to ensure a fine mist. If the mist falls in droplets or is sprayed too close to your client they will experience a heat reaction which may cause discomfort.

5. Apply tip for your desired look. Tip should be applied at a 45° degree angle at the free edge and rock forward, holding down until secure. Cut the tip to the required length using edge cutters.

Figure 12.14 Applying resin

Figure 12.15 Spraying with activator

Figure 12.16 Trimming the fibreglass strip

Figure 12.17 Trimming the nail

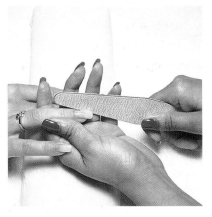

Figure 12.18 Filing the nail into shape

6. Apply a small amount of resin to the re-growth area and spread using the nozzle for control.

7. Spray with activator being careful not to spray too close.

8. If the nail is in perfect condition, apply a small strip of fibreglass in the re-growth area only. If the nail needs strengthening apply fibreglass to the whole of the nail. If there is no crack in the free edge apply a stress strip to this area and the re-growth area.

9. Apply resin over the mesh, starting at the cuticle and continuing to the free edge. The mesh will turn transparent when fully saturated. Keep the product away from the cuticle area.

10. Spray with activator.

11. Repeat steps 9 and 10.

12. File gently into shape using a soft grit file.

13. Buff gently with a block buffer and bring to a shine with a three-way shiner.

14. Apply cuticle oil to rehydrate cuticles.

Maintenance of fibreglass

Two weeks after application:

1. Sanitise your hands and those of your client.

2. Remove any nail enamel using acetone-free enamel remover and check for any signs of infection.

3. Push back the cuticles with a hoof stick or orange stick tipped with cotton wool.

4. Buff the re-growth area using a medium grit file to remove any loose or lifted fibreglass. It is important to blend the seam until invisible to avoid marks in the finished nail. Buff the whole nail to remove shine.

5. Apply a small amount of resin in the re-growth area and spread over the whole re-growth area using the nozzle for control.

6. Spray with activator being careful not to hold it too close.

7. Apply resin over the whole of the nail from cuticle to free edge. Spread as before.

8. Spray with activator.

9. Buff gently with a block buffer and bring to shine with a three-way shiner.

10. Apply cuticle oil to rehydrate the cuticles.

Four weeks after initial application:

1. Sanitise your hands and those of your client.

2. Remove nail enamel using acetone-free enamel remover and check for signs of infection.

3. Push back the cuticles using a hoof stick or orange stick tipped with cotton wool.

4. Buff the re-growth area using a medium grit file to remove any loose or lifted fibreglass.

5. Blend seam area using a coarse grit file. Be careful to blend the tip only and not into the nail plate.

6. Apply a coat of resin to the nail plate and spray with activator.

TIP: To prevent damage occurring when filing the nail extension, be careful not to touch the nail plate.

193

7. Apply fibreglass/silk mesh to entire nail, keeping mesh 2 mm away from the sidewalls and cuticle. Cut, using sharp scissors to avoid fraying.

8. Apply resin over the mesh. Start at the cuticle and continue to the free edge. The mesh will turn transparent when fully saturated. Keep the product away from the cuticle area.

9. Spray with activator.

10. Repeat steps 8–9 for resin and spray until the desired shape is achieved and there are no mesh indentations visible (approximately three times in total).

11. Using a soft grit file, shape and buff the nail surface briefly.

12. Bring to a shine with three-way shiner. Apply cuticle oil to rehydrate the cuticles.

13. Ask your client to wash their hands to remove oil as the polish will not adhere to the nail, if oily.

14. You are now ready to paint.

Fibreglass problem solving

▌ *White areas under the nail tip*. This could be due to air bubbles trapped during application of the nail tip. You will have to remove the tip and reapply. Use slightly more thin tip glue.

▌ *Fibreglass mesh shows through the finished nail*. This can happen if the first coat of thin tip glue was not absorbed through the fibre mesh, or if the fibreglass was handled too much before application.

▌ *Lifting of the fibreglass overlay*. This may be due to products touching the cuticle or nail wall if too much adhesive was used, or not enough glue to encase the fibre mesh may also cause this problem.

▌ *Frayed fibreglass mesh*. If the mesh has frayed through the adhesive, it could be that the scissors were not sharp enough, or that the fibreglass was not pressed smooth to the nail before thin tip glue was applied and raised holes appear.

GEL NAILS

Light cured procedure

Gel can be applied over tips or sculptured onto nail forms as with acrylic. Some gel systems require the use of an ultraviolet light to set, while others use a spray activator.

1. Sanitise you hands and those of your client.

2. Remove polish and check for contra-indications (see pages 184–185).

3. Push back the cuticles and lightly buff the surface to remove shine.

4. Apply tips and blend.

5. Apply primer if recommended by gel manufacturer.

6. Apply gel. Brush gel onto the entire nail and cover with a thin even layer as you would nail polish. Keep product away from the cuticle as it will lift.

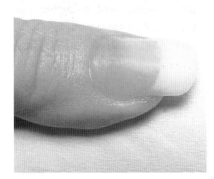

Figure 12.19 Air bubbles trapped beneath the nail

Figure 12.20 Fibreglass mesh showing through the finished nail

Figure 12.21 Frayed fibreglass mesh

Figure 12.22 Gel application

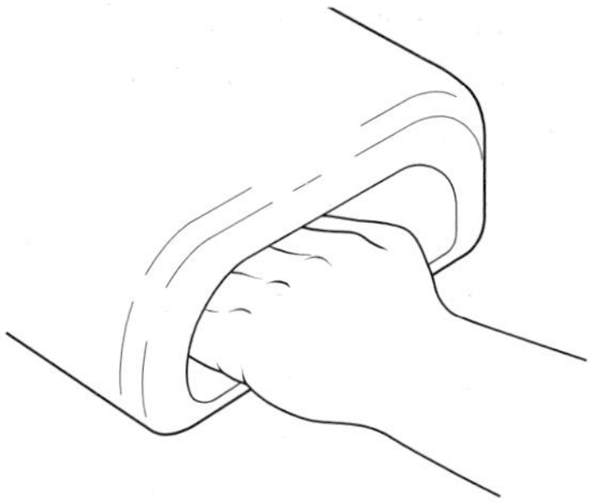

Figure 12.23 Curing gel under UV lamp

7. Cure gel. Place nails under the lamp for the time recommended by the manufacturer.

8. Apply second coat of gel.

9. Cure gel.

10. Apply a third coat of gel and cure.

11. Clean the nails by wiping with alcohol or manufacturer's recommended cleanser to remove any residue and tackiness on cured nails. Cured nails have a shiny gloss that needs no buffing if applied smoothly.

12. Apply cuticle oil.

Maintenance procedure

Maintenance to the gel nails should be carried out approximately every two weeks.

1. Sanitise your hands and those of your client.

2. Remove any polish and check for signs of infection.

3. Push back cuticle and buff re-growth area to remove any loose or lifting gel using a fine grit file. Buff the whole nail with a medium grit file to remove any shine and to prevent product build up.

4. Apply primer to this area only.

5. Apply a small bead of gel near the cuticle. This should be a thin application to avoid any ridge forming. Brush new application of gel towards the free edge.

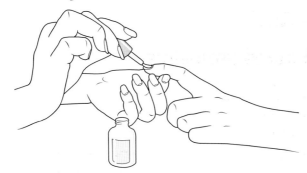

Figure 12.24 Applying gel during maintenance

6. Cure gel.

7. Remove sticky residue.

8. Use a three-way shiner if necessary to shine.

9. Apply cuticle oil.

TIP: The procedure recommended for applying and curing gel varies from one manufacturer to another. Some systems recommend applying the gel to four nails on one hand and curing, then repeating the procedure on the other hand before applying and curing the thumb nails. Other manufacturers provide light systems that cure one finger at a time. Be sure to follow the instructions recommended for the system you are using.

TIP: If the client's gel is uneven after curing, check your application technique.

AFTERCARE

Aftercare advice for your client should include the following information:

I Use rubber gloves when cleaning or washing up.

I Do not use fingernails as tools.

I Use only acetone-free enamel remover. Acetone will soften the nail extension and lead to lifting.

I Caution should be used when near a naked flame or excessive heat as the extensions can melt.

I Always use a base coat under the nail enamel to avoid yellowing.

I Do not pull the nails off if they start to lift; have them removed professionally and safely.

Removing artificial nails

1. Your client should wash their hands.
2. Remove any existing nail enamel.
3. Cut off any artificial free edge.
4. Slightly roughen the surface of the nail with a medium grit file, to encourage absorption of the solvent.
5. Place the fingertips in a glass bowl containing acetone and a teaspoon of oil. Acetone dehydrates the skin and nail plates; oil helps to soften and lubricate the skin and nails as they are taken from the bowl.
6. Every 3–4 minutes remove the fingers and wipe away the dissolving artificial nail with a tissue soaked in acetone.
7. The nail should be completely dissolved in about 10–15 minutes. A full manicure and the application of a strengthener should be carried out to ensure that your client leaves the salon with their nails in the best possible condition and rehydrated.

SUMMARY

From the content of this chapter you will have established the range of technological advances, particularly in the area of nail extensions, and developments in nail extension techniques. This is an area in which the technician must constantly strive to maintain their awareness of new developments and introductions.

FURTHER STUDY

1. Define each of the following:

I disinfection

I sanitation

I sterilisation.

2. List the contra-indication checks that you would make before applying artificial nails.
3. Research nail art and try out some of the techniques.
4. Design a treatment plan for the application and maintainance of artificial nails.
5. Draw a diagram to illustrate the blood circulation to the forearm and hand and that of the foot and lower leg.

6. Identify the functions of the blood. Define:

   a. a vein

   b. an artery.

7. Research the various styles used to decorate the nails. Look at Nail Art and French manicures in particular.

8. Find out about different nail tips available. Record the benefits of each.

9. French tips are very popular. Find out how the application of product varies to accommodate tips in fibreglass and acrylic.

10. Contra-indications are adverse conditions that appears after nails have been applied. Describe the following:

    a thinning of the nail plate

    b. softening of the nail plate

    c. allergies

    d. infection of the nail plate

    e. physical trauma to the nail plate cuticle and nail bed.

Review questions

1. Name the two bones of the forearm.

2. What is the hardened protein of the nails?

3. Give 3 hygiene precautions to be followed when applying artificial nails.

4. Why is positioning of the client vital to a successful treatment?

5. How would you repair a weak tip and a split in the free edge?

6. Detail the aftercare advice you would give the client.

7. Give three causes of lifting of a nail extension.

8. What causes air bubbles in the acrylic and how would you avoid them?

9. What advice would you give to your client about the frequency of maintenance for nail extensions?

13

Heat treatments

If you plan to work in a health farm, club or fitness related establishment then the treatments in this chapter will prove to be both popular and useful in your treatment planning. Warming the body tissues prior to further treatment will improve the overall result, this is because when the body is warm the skin's resistance is lowered making application easier and more effective.

Health and leisure centres are more popular as today's pace of life is becoming increasingly hectic therefore there is a need to relax and unwind. Heat treatments offer both therapeutic and social advantages to help you do this.

Level 3

Elements

20.1 Advise on dry and wet heat treatments

20.2 Prepare for dry and wet heat treatments

20.3 Monitor dry and wet heat treatments

13.1 Maintain safe working practices within the salon

CONTENTS

Heat treatments	199
Sauna	200
Steam	201
Spa Pool	203
Paraffin wax	203
Infra Red Light	205
Summary	205
Further Study	206
Review Questions	206

HEAT TREATMENTS

Heat may be applied in two ways

Locally to individual
body parts eg. infra red
or paraffin wax.

Generally to the
whole body e.g.
steam bath or sauna

The General Effects of Heating the Body

Ⅰ Increase in cellular metabolism hence oxygen is brought to the area and waste products are taken away.

Ⅰ Stimulation of glandular activity hence there will be an improvement in skin texture.

Ⅰ A rise in general body temperature.

Ⅰ Hyperaemia (pink colouring) due to the increase in blood flow to the area.

Ⅰ The body tissues will be more receptive to further treatment as resistance is lowered.

Ⅰ Soothes and relaxes the client.

Ⅰ Reduces appetite.

Ⅰ Blood pressure falls.

Ⅰ Pulse rate increases.

The extent of the effects produced will be dependant on:

1. The size of the area being treated.

2. The duration of treatment.

3. The intensity of treatment.

4. The chosen method.

Each treatment will have it's own specific contraindications but some of the general ones are as follows:

Ⅰ Any medical condition without the consent your client's G.P.

Ⅰ A high body temperature or if your client feels feverish. e.g. flu

Ⅰ Skin disorders and diseases e.g. verucca and Athletes foot.

Ⅰ Pregnancy or menstruation may require the consent of your client's G.P.

Ⅰ Following a heavy meal or alcohol.

Ⅰ Any medical condition that may be aggravated by heat. e.g. eczema, diabetes, migrane and epilepsy.

Ⅰ Inflammatory conditions.

Ⅰ Respiratory abnormalities. e.g. asthma.

Heat may be applied to the body in the form of **dry** or **moist** heat or **hydrotherapy**.

Type of heat applied	example
Dry	Sauna
Moist	Steam Room
Hydrotherapy	Whirl pool

TIP: The working temperature of the sauna will vary as follows:

70°C   mild

90°C   strong

110°C   very strong.

TIP: Remain within calling distance of your client and inform them that you will be nearby should they require help.

TIP: The golden rule in sauna is the lower the benches the lower the temperature.

TIP: Do not allow your client to walk about in bare feet as fungal infections thrive in moist conditions. Provide them with disposable slippers or sanitised flip flops.

TIP: The larger the sauna the more it costs to run.

TIP: Humidity refers to the moisture content of the air.

SAUNA

This treatment which uses the benefits of dry heat is usually a communal treatment. It possible for up to 14 people to use the sauna cabin at one time hence one of it's specific effects is social but more importantly the warmth produced will help to relax your client whilst deep cleansing the skin and detoxifying.

The cabin is made of pine wood logs and heat is provided by an electric stove. Pine wood will allow the interchange of air and absorbs moisture, this results in 'dry heat'. Your client may control the humidity within the cabin by pouring water onto the electric stove therefore temperature will fluctuate between 50–120 °C according to her tolerance.

Specific Effects

I A fall in blood pressure

I An increase in perspiration hence elimination of waste products

I Metabolism speeds up

I Increase in heart rate

I Relaxation of nerve endings hence sedative effect

I Dehydration if treatment is excessive

I Rise in body temperature

I A general sense of well being

Specific Contra indications

I Disease or disorder of the skin e.g athletes foot

I Abnormal blood pressure

I Claustrophobia

I Heart or circulatory problems

I Respiratory or chest conditions

I Pregnancy

I Crash dieting

I Headaches, dizziness, migranes or fainting

Application of treatment

During consultation check with your client for contra indications and explain the treatment using non-technical language. Ensure your client understands and agrees to the treatment.

1. Ask your client to shower prior to their treatment and have a clean robe and pair of disposable slippers ready for them to wear.

2. Ensure that you have pre-heated the sauna to a comfortable temperature at least 1 hour before your client's arrival.

3. Check that your client has removed contact lenses, glasses, jewellery, etc.

4. Your client may wish to cover their hair before entering the sauna. Ensure that your client sits on a towel for hygiene purposes.

5. Treatment duration will vary according to client tolerance but normal treatment will last for 15–20 minutes to include several trips to the shower at regular intervals.

6. Following their treatment your client should be advised to rest on a couch until their body temperature returns to normal.

Maintenance of the Sauna

1. Ensure the sauna is scrubbed with disinfectant regularly

2. Keep a bucket of water full up inside the sauna.

3. When switched off, open the sauna doors to allow for the circulation of fresh air and prevent unfriendly odours.

4. Ensure the shower area is regularly cleaned with disinfectant and the appropriate consumables are at hand e.g. shower gel.

TIP: All surfaces should be wiped over before and after use with disinfectant.

Figure 13.2 A sauna

STEAM TREATMENT

This treatment uses the benefits of 'moist heat' in the form of steam which may be applied to your client in the following ways:

I Vapour treatment – used for treating individual areas.

I Steam bath   – used for treating the body but excluding the head.

I Steam room   – used for treating the whole body.

N.B. The vapour treatment is described in the facial treatments chapter on page 66.

Specific Effects

I Induces relaxation

I Deep cleanses the skin

I Softens Skin tissue

I Aids absorption of products

I Reduce the skin's resistance if given prior to an electrical treatment.

I Hyperaemia (redness of the skin)

I Body temperature increases.

I Pulse rate speeds up

I Blood pressure lowered

I Metabolism increases

I Stimulation of glandular activity

I Desquamation is increased.

The steam bath

The steam bath offers a more personal treatment as it treats the individual, your client sits inside the cabinet that is usually made of fibre glass (sometimes metal) and their head remains outside the cabinet at all times.

This is ideal if your client is slightly claustrophobic as they continues to breath in normal air. The door is hinged and never locked so that your client is free to open and get out as and when they wish. The temperature may be adjusted to suit the individual's needs and tolerance.

You will prepare the steam bath prior to your client's arrival, using distilled water to cover the element in the metal box at the bottom of the cabinet. When switched on the water heats up and produces steam, the air in the cabinet being saturated with humidity at around 95%. Treatment may last between 10–20 minutes depending on client tolerance.

The steam bath is an ideal treatment for small salons at it takes up little space and cost less to run compared with the steam room.

The steam room

The steam room may be found in health farms, hydros and fitness centers. It offers a more communal treatment as up to eight people may be treated at once. Because of its size the steam room is obviously more expensive to operate and it offers the advantage of your client being able to lie down if they so wish.

Your clients hair will get wet and they will breath in the humid air throughout the treatment.

Specific Contra indications to Steam treatment

I After a heavy meal especially if it included alcohol

I During the first few days of menstruation

I The late stages of pregnancy

I Epilepsy

I Diabetes

I Headache or migraine sufferers

I Certain skin disorders can be improved if exposed to wet heat but G.P. referral is always recommended first.

I Respiratory conditions e.g. Asthma

I Thrombosis or phlebitis

I Heart conditions

I Abnormal blood pressure

I Skin disorders or diseases e.g. Verrucas , Athletes foot

I Sunburn or over exposure to ultra violet light.

I Claustrophobia

TIP: Advise the client not to touch the metal box in the steam cabinet.

TIP: The ideal temperature for a steam treatment is 45°C.

Application of treatment

N.B. the steam bath should be wiped over before and after use with disinfectant. All surfaces should be covered with a towel or couch roll.

1. Switch on the steam room or cabinet prior to your client's arrival. If using the steam cabinet, cover the element with water.

2. After a thorough consultation, ask your client to take shower and provide them with a robe and disposable slippers. They should remove all jewellery, contact lenses, glasses etc.

3. Provided your client is not contraindicated, show your client how to enter and leave the steam area. If they are having a steam bath help them in and place a rolled towel around the top of the cabinet, around their neck.

4. Ensuring your client is comfortable, switch the timer on (10–15 mins) and adjust the temperature control if necessary.

5. Always remain with in calling distance.

6. On completion of treatment, help your client out of the cabinet and guide them to the shower.

7. Advise your client to rest for 15–30 minutes and offer a drink of cold water.

Maintainence of the steam bath/room

There is a high risk of cross infection as moist heat will provide a breeding ground for micro-organisms, especially fungal infections. Always offer your client disposable footware or the type of shoe that may be easily santised.

The area needs to be disinfected before and after each client and as with the sauna it is advisable to leave the door open when not in use to allow natural air to circulate.

SPA POOL

This treatment may sometimes be referred to as a whirlpool or jacuzzi. They may be found mainly in health clubs, and health farms offering a relaxing communal treatment.

The size of the spa will vary but it basically consists of a large bath in which pumps, force air through holes in the side of the tank which aerate the water and massage the surface of the skin.

Effects of treatment include:

| Relaxation

| Stimulation of sweat glands

| Erythema (redness of the skin)

| Raised body temperature

N.B. for contra indications and maintenance please refer to previous heat treatments.

PARAFFIN WAX

This treatment may be applied to the face or body and serves to relax your client as it softens the surface of the skin. It is ideal for isolated areas of pain such as the lower back or arthritic joints as it stimulates the circulation in the area where it is applied. The wax is usually warmed in a purpose built heater which is thermostatically controlled to a working temperature of 45–49°C.

> **TIP: Remain within calling distance of your client and inform them that you will be nearby should they require help.**

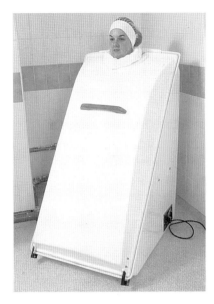

Figure 13.2 Steam cabinet with client

> **TIP: Steam cabinets are made of metal or fibreglass.**

TIP: Always test a small patch on wrist first and on your client to ensure a comfortable temperature.

TIP: Never be tempted to re-use the wax it is impossible to sterilised sufficiently.

TIP: Check the temperature of the wax frequently as it will ignite if it becomes too hot!

TIP: If decanting into a bowl before applying, ensure that this is placed on a stable base.

TIP: If working from a bowl, grease the inside of the bowl first and line with foil or polythene.

The wax is applied with a sterilised brush in several layers or if treating the hands or feet, the limb may be immersed into the wax.

As a precautionary measure, you should always test the wax on the inside of your wrist before applying to your client and ensure that you have prepared your area with disposable tissue to catch any drips during application.

Once a thick layer has been applied, you should wrap the area in foil or polythene and then wrap with a warm towel to retain the heat.

Specific Effects of Paraffin Wax

I Soothes and relaxes

I Stimulates sebaceous secretion

I The wax itself moisturises the skin

I Redness due to vasodilation

I Increases metabolism

I Desquamates.

Contra indications Specific To Paraffin Wax

There are few contra indications to paraffin wax which makes it a very popular treatment.

I Open cuts and abrasions

I Severe bruising

I Skin infection or diseases

I Excessively hairy areas

I Areas of pain without the consent of your client's G.P.

Maintenance of Paraffin Wax

After use always dispose of soiled wax and never attempt to re-use it even on the same client.

Never pour melted wax down the sink as it may block the pipes.

On occasions when the wax heater is empty and allow to cool, wipe clean with disinfectant and re-fill with new blocks of wax.

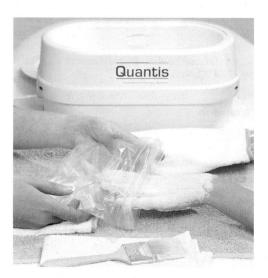

Figure 13.3 Using a paraffin wax heater

INFRA-RED LIGHT

These rays are electromagnetic wavelengths between 700 and 400,000nm and the lamps that produce these rays can be divided into two main types:

I Non-luminous or infra red

I Luminous or radiant heat (rarely used in Beauty Therapy).

Specific Uses of Infra-red light

Infra-red equipment is used for:

I promotion of relaxation

I encourage absorption of applied products

I relieve pain and tension in muscle tissue

I render the tissues more receptive for body treatments.

Specific contra-indications

I abnormal blood pressure

I defective circulation

I lack of sensation (includes recent scar tissue)

I hypersensitivity

I heart conditions

I late pregnancy (last trimester)

I disease/disorders of the skin

I feverish conditions, e.g. flu, migraine etc.

I diabetes.

TIP: Before use always check electrical equipment for obvious damage or fault. Any fault should be reported to the person responsible and the equipment taken out of action.

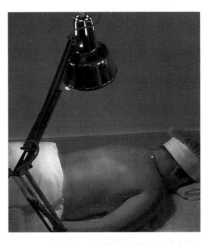

Figure 13.4 Infra-red lamp treatment

Treatment Application

1. Ensure that your client is comfortable on the couch with jewellery removed. Protect their eyes and areas not to be treated.

2. Degrease the treatment area and check carefully for contra-indication. Ensure that your client can distinguish between hot and cold.

3. Remind your client that you will remain with them throughout the treatment and that they must not touch the lamp, as it will be hot.

4. Ensuring that the lamp is stable and pointing away from the client, turn it on and allow to warm up.

5. Position the lamp parallel to the treatment area so that the rays penetrate best at 90 degrees.

6. Provided that the heat is tolerable, exposure may be up to 15 minutes duration.

SUMMARY

This chapter has given you and insight into the range of heat treatments that might be used in the salon or health and fitness sector. You should now feel equipped to select the most suitable treatment to offer your client, in order to suit their condition and needs having the confidence to be able to give accurate advice on the chosen method.

You will find heat treatments a useful compliment to your figure treatments, they are easy to link sell to your client and they will speed up results!

FURTHER STUDY

1. Research additional heat treatments that may be used in the salon such as a floatation tank and hydrotherapy bath. How much do they cost? What type of establishment might use them?

2. Give four signs and symptoms of a client suffering from heat exhaustion.

3. Draw a diagram to represent the electromagnetic spectrum.

4. Describe three contra actions to dry and wet heat treatments.

5. Explain the production of dry heat in a sauna.

6. Explain how vasodilation occurs.

7. Describe what is happening in the body when
   i)   the pulse rate increases
   ii) the blood pressure falls.

8. Find out the first aid procedure for a client suffering from the following:
   i)   dehydration
   ii)   nausea
   iii) fainting.

Review Questions

1. State six precautionary measures to be taken when using heat treatments.

2. Explain the advantages of offering a heat treatment before an electrical one.

3. Give six effects on a healthy adult of general body heating.

4. Describe the application of infra red light to the upper back.

5. List five differences between a sauna and a steam cabinet.

6. When a healthy adult takes a sauna, state whether or not
   i)   the pulse rate goes up or down
   ii) the blood pressure is lowered.

7. List the factors that determine the effectiveness of a heat treatment.

8. Give one example of the following heat treatments
   i)   Hydrotherapy
   ii)   Dry heat
   iii) Moist heat.

Ultra violet tanning treatments

Sunbeds have become technologically advanced over recent years. They may be shaped to fit the contours of the body enabling your client to tan the sides as well as her back and front.

There is great controversy regarding the use of sunbeds in our industry, it's therefore vital, that you are well informed and confident in your knowledge regarding this treatment. Your client will expect you to describe the benefits and uses of ultra violet light and you may be required to recognise the dangers of over exposure.

Level 3

Elements

13.1 Maintain safe working practices within the salon

21.1 Advise clients on UV tanning

21.2 Prepare the treatment area and client for UV tanning

21.3 Monitor UV tanning sessions

CONTENTS

Ultra violet radiation	208
Specific Effects	208
Preparation of Treatment Area	209
Preparation of Client	209
Basic safety rules	210
Summary	211
Further Study	211
Review Questions	211

ULTRA VIOLET RADIATION

These rays are part of the electromagnetic spectrum with wave lengths of between 400nm and 10nm and are divided into three bands.

UVA = the longest wave length (315–400nm) These rays penetrate the skin's dermis and have a tanning effect on the skin. However, these rays are far from harmless, they will destroy connective tissue i.e. collagen and elastin fibres which are responsible for the youthful appearance of the skin hence over exposure will accelerate the ageing process, causing wrinkles. It is also thought that these rays will increase the risk of skin cancers. There is more UVA than UVB in natural sunlight and UVA can penetrate glass, therefore, you are exposed to irradiation if you stand near a window or sit in a car.

UVB = the middle band (280nm–315nm). Penetrates the epidermis as far as the basal layer and has the ability to tan and burn the skin. It is also responsible for thickening of the skin and the development of skin cancers. It is these rays that are the most intense in the midday sun, when the sun is closest to earth. These rays may also cause wrinkles and cholasma.

UVC = these are the shortest wave lengths (below 280 nm) These rays will penetrate the epidermis but are not found in natural sun light as they are absorbed by the Earth's atmosphere (the ozone layer). These rays are not used in sunbeds and are potentially the most damaging.

Ultraviolet radiation is available from sunlight, sunbeds, solariums and sun lamps. The sunbed consists of two rows florescent tubes, each tube is lined with phosphorus and is positioned in front of a metal reflector. Ultraviolet light travels in straight lines and the purpose of the phosphorous coating is to absorb UVB and UVC only allowing UVA to pass through.

A fast tanning sunbed will emit mainly UVA but allow some UVB to pass through, this allows your client to receive a quicker and longer lasting tan.

Figure 14.1 A sunbed tube

Specific Effects of UV Exposure

The degree of effect will be dependant on the duration of treatment and your client's skin type.

I Redness due to the increase in blood flow. This is a normal reaction to irradiation however, erythema may occur up to 12 hours after exposure.

I Thickening of the skin. The penetration of UVB increased the rate of mitosis in the basal layer of the epidermis, these cells push upwards resulting in a visible thickening of the horny layer.

I Accelerated desquamation. This effect is linked to the thickening of the skin, as the horny layer builds up, the rate of desquamation increases.

I A general sense of well being and relaxation. The warmth of irradiation contributes towards the sedative effect of this treatment resulting in reduced irritability.

I Production of vitamin D is accelerated. This vitamin is essential for the absorption of calcium, playing a vital role in the growth and development of bones and teeth.

I Premature ageing. UVB has an adverse effect on connective tissue, the fibres of collagen and elastin which play a vital role in maintaining a youthful appearance of the skin will be damaged.

- Skin cancer. Evidence clearly suggests that exposure to UV light may cause cancer. It has been found that irradiation interrupts the DNA in the nucleus of the cells causing disease.

- Sunburn if over exposed. Over exposure will cause burning of the skin.

- Dehydration of the skin. This refers to the loss of the skin's natural moisture content.

- Allergic reaction. Some individuals suffer an unusual reaction to exposure to UV light, they experience irritation just a few hours after irradiation, resulting in itchy papules. This condition usually clears itself over 2–6 days.

- Hyperpigmentation. This is the result of hyperactivity of the melanocytes in the epidermis resulting in brown patches.

- Mildly germicidal hence healing effect. Exposure to UV light will improve certain skin conditions e.g. psoriasis.

- Tanning. This is not an immediate effect of irradiation as pigmentation develops 1–2 days after exposure.

> TIP: Remember everyone is at risk from UV damage.

> TIP: Peoples attitude to tanning began to change as late as the 1920s, when Coco Chanel first caused a sensation in Paris and around the world by showing her clothing on tanned models.

Eye damage

Not only will UV damage the delicate skin around the eyes but may also cause conjunctivitis (inflammation of the conjunctiva of the eye) and Keratitis (inflammation of the cornea of the eye). You have a responsibility of care to ensure your client wears the goggles supplied.

Preparation of the equipment

Regularly check the sunbed is working, test the timer and on/off switch.

The bed must be wiped over with disinfectant before use and sanitised goggles must be provided for each client. Warm towels and disposable slippers should be made available.

Pay particular attention to the room ventilation it is essential that natural air flows freely as the treatment room will become very warm.

> TIP: Up to two thirds of our lifetime are spent involuntarily exposed to UV that occurs in our every day activities, i.e. driving, gardening, walking etc.

Client preparation and and application

1. Ensure that you wipe over the sunbeds surfaces with an appropriate cleaning agent. These are available from the manufacturer's.

2. When your client arrives explain the treatment and complete the record card and ascertain how they normally react to sunlight, what skin type they have e.g. fair, medium or dark and finally whether they have recently been exposed to UV light.

3. Check that your client is not contraindicated. Specific Contraindications include:

- Pregnancy
- The inability to tan effectively
- Pigmentation problems such as vitiligo
- Heart conditions
- Claustrophobia
- Epilepsy
- Abnormal blood pressure
- Medication e.g. antibiotics, tranquillisers, steroids, contraceptive pill (seek G.P'.s advice), insulin, gold vaccinations, quinine, diuretics, blood pressure medication and thyroid medication.

> TIP: Take time to explain the importance of wearing goggles.

> TIP: Check the sunbed regularly ensuring the tubes are emitting light effectively and always refer to the manufacturer's recommendations when replacing them. Always employ professional expertise to undertake these functions.

4. In the interest of hygiene encourage your client to shower and dry their skin prior to treatment. This will also guarantee removal of body lotions and perfumes which may affect the evenness of the tan.

5. Ensure that your client has removed their contact lenses and jewellery etc and that they must wear the goggles provided. Your client may wish to cover their hair, especially if it is chemically treated.

6. Switch on the sunbed and remain within calling distance. If this treatment is their first, then it is advisable to keep the dose short i.e. 15–20 minutes in duration.

7. On completion of treatment encourage your client to rest until their body temperature returns to normal. Suggest the application of a moisturising lotion.

8. Complete your client's record card stating date of treatment, time of treatment and reaction treatment.

BASIC SAFETY RULES WHEN EXPOSING THE BODY TO NATURAL SUNLIGHT

It is likely that your client will book a course of sunbeds prior to going on holiday, it is worthwhile offering them the following useful advice:

1. Always use a protective sun cream and re-apply regularly.

2. Avoid the midday sun.

3. However tempted you are, do not sunbathe for long periods.

4. Keep covered if possible i.e. sunglasses to protect the eyes, wide brimmed hats, cotton sleeved shirts but remember when fabrics are wet their protection is reduced.

5. Children and babies are most vulnerable so keep them covered up.

Sunscreens

These creams work by absorbing harmful UVB and UVC rays. The type and concentration of active ingredients will vary according to the different levels of protection required. This protection is referred to as S.P.F. (sun protection factor) the higher the SPF the more protection.

They are available in gel, lotion or cream form.

Sunblock

These products contain powders such as zinc and kaolin in a cream base and serve to reflect harmful rays.

Fake tans

Dihydroxyacetone is a white powder with a characteristic smell which dissolved in alcohol forms a colourless solution but turns brown by oxidation when spread on to the skin. The only 'safe' tan is obtained from the bottle and these have become increasingly popular over recent years.

The product must be applied correctly after a thorough exfoliation of the area and as your client's skin will naturally desquamate, fake tan may need to be reapplied regularly.

TIP: There is no doubt that the sun does damage your skin.

TIP: Skin cancers are less common in people with dark skins e.g. Spaniards, Greeks, etc. these people are at less risk because their skin contains more melanin.

TIP: Despite public awareness of the dangers of UV exposure, it has been proven that most of us look for the resort that offers the maximum sunshine when choosing a holiday.

SUMMARY

This chapter has given you an insight into the effects of UV light, you should now realize the importance of monitoring treatments closely and ensuring that your client is adequately protected while receiving treatment in your salon. If your client should suffer a contra-action, the treatment should be discontinued and appropriate remedial action taken. Finally, it is vital that you keep your client's records up to date and give them the appropriate aftercare advice regarding application of a moisturiser and avoidence of any other heat treatment immediately after a sunbed treatment.

Figure 14.2 Wearing goggles

FURTHER STUDY

1. Find a picture of a mercury vapour lamp and explain how it works.
2. Explain the following in relation to radiation treatments:-
   i)   The law of Inverse Square.
   ii) The Cosine Law.
   iii) The Law of Grotthus.
3. Explain why the following are contra indications to UV exposure:
   i)   the contraceptive pill
   ii) claustrophobia
   iii) steroids
   iv) epilepy.
4. Distinguish between refraction and reflection.
5. Find out about the three types of skin cancer.
6. Explain how a solarium differs from a sunbed.

REVIEW QUESTIONS

1. Give four physiological effects of UV rays.
2. Describe the preparation of your client prior to a sunbed treatment.
3. Why are children more vulnerable to skin damage from natural sunlight?
4. State the wave lengths of each of the following: UVA, UVB and UVC.
5. State the band of rays which has the deepest penetration.
6. Describe how a sun block works.
7. Explain the steps you would take if your client has a contra-action to a sunbed treatment in the salon.
8. A client arrives at your salon she has never had a sunbed before and thinks their skin is quite sensitive. Outline the advice you would give them.

15 | Model answers

CHAPTER 1

None

CHAPTER 2

1. Acknowledge their presence and then complete your transaction with your client; it may be possible to seek a colleague's assistance in responding to the newly arrived client.

2. Excuse yourself from the sales representative and immediately respond to the client or ensure that a colleague is providing them with assistance.

3. Fidgeting, facial grimacing or pulling away.

4. Questioning which encourages explanatory responses, more than yes/no answers.

5. Client's name, contact address, contact telephone number, details of the analysis, any contra-indications, treatment recommendations (including type of treatment, products to be used, time-scale for programme), recommended homecare products any doctor's consent forms.

6. Statements from clients confirming good service

7. Any of the following:
   I quality of service
   I cost of service
   I value for money
   I speed of service

| | quality of salon environment
| | range of service available

CHAPTER 3

1. Using a clean sterile spatula.

2. Trade Descriptions Act 1968.

3. Scrape eye shadow from the block onto a palette or spatula before use.

4. Review and negotiate future performance.

5. Report this to the person responsible (complete a hazard report) and remove the equipment from use.

6. Sale of Goods Act

7. Kept confidential and stored securely

8. By your example, demonstration

CHAPTER 4

1. The employer.

2. The Local Government (Miscellaneous Provisions) Act 1982.

3. Infection which is spread from one person to another via contaminated materials and equipment. The risk is reduced by maintaining high levels of hygiene in the salon and ensuring that everything which comes in contact with the client is cleaned and whenever practicable sterilised before it contacts another.

4. Cleaned and dried (washed or wiped with cleaning agent).

5. A waterproof dressing.

6. This causes a very slippery surface upon which someone may slip.

7. Read the manufacturer's guidelines in its use, seek guidance from your supervisor.

8. Powder, Carbon Dioxide or BCF.

CHAPTER 5

1. To keep informed of special offers and so that you may contact in an emergency.

2. Prolonged exposure to ozone may be carcinogenic, see effects on page 66–67.

3. See page 69.

4. When performing vacuum suction you should stop your stroke just before the lymph node.

5. The skin type that would benefit from desincrustation may be dry/sensitive, normal/combination and oily/problem.

6. Iontophoresis works by introducing water soluble substances into the skin.

7. See page 76.

8. Vapour treatment may be used to pre heat the skin locally.

CHAPTER 6

1. Cheese, Full cream milk, butter animal fat.

2. Having been converted to monosaccarides it is used for energy or stored in the body as fat.

3. 2 litres.

4. If your client finds a full press up too difficult, suggest she adapts to a box press up on her knees.

5. Double leg lifting is dangerous because:

   The lower back is put under great stress.

   The exerciser often holds her breath.

   The abdominals are distended forwards and tremble.

6. Look at how she cooks her food advise on grilling and boiling as oppose to frying.

   Ensure that she includes all essential vitamins and minerals as well as fibre.

   Check that she is drinking plenty of water.

   Cut down on smoking.

7. Good muscle tone refers to the continuous slight tension of the muscle tissue and is involuntary . Good muscle tone is essential for maintaining good posture.

8. We need flexibility from youth into old age. We need to be able to reach up to a shelf and pick up a dropped article. Regular stretching prevents injury and improves co ordination.

CHAPTER 7

1. Suitable resting period.

   Drink plenty of water.

   Try not to do anything too physically demanding immediately following the massage.

2. Remove medium immediately.

   Document details of contra action on client's record card.

   If problem persists refer your client to her G.P.

3. Redness, locally on the area.

4. To be seen to be hygienic will inspire confidence in your client.

5. Help on and off the couch.

   Keep warm.

   Assistance when turning your client over.

   If the client lacks a heavy covering of adipose tissue avoid percussion movements.

   Stay close by the client.

CHAPTER 8

1. a) Personal details will enable you to:-

   File their treatment plan correctly.

   Contact them in an emergency.

   Keep them informed of special offers and discounts.

1. b) Medical details will enable you to :-

   Check for contra indications.

   Seek G.P.'s approval if required.

   Adapt treatment if areas are restricted.

2. A varicose vein results when the thin walls of the vein have become pushed outwards and lose their elasticity through over stretching.

3. See facial chapter Fig 5.4.

4. Ensure that the controls are at zero before you turn up the intensity.

   Always test the machine on yourself before you apply the treatment to your client.

   If a fault occurs during use, turn off power and call an electrician.

   Ensure equipment is correctly earthed. (Double insulation)

   Have equipment regularly serviced.

   Follow manufacturer's instructions.

   Avoid using adaptors.

   Have equipment professionally installed.

5. One teaspoon of salt to one pint of distilled water.

6. Electrodes incorrectly positioned.

   Inadequate conductor on electrodes.

   Barrier on the skin, i.e. grease.

   Machine not switched on.

   Intensity too low.

   Straps not secure.

   Electrodes not in full contact with skin.

7. Faradic type, G5 and vacuum suction combined with a heat treatment.

8. Exercise plan

   Constructive advice on diet and healthy eating plan.

CHAPTER 9

1. Gamma Radiation, Ethylene Oxide Gas.

2. In a sharps box, that is hygienically disposed of.

3. Client's pain threshold, hair type and texture, area to be treated, skin type being treated.

4. Sterex disposable needle.

5. To ensure accurate probing, to check needle for damage – prior to use.

6. Inaccurate probing, insufficient current intensity, missed hairs, over probing, application time too short, too shallow probing.

7. Direct current.

8. Heat – produced by a high frequency, oscillating alternating current.

9. Clients may undertake treatments which may cause a reaction to already sensitised skin.

10. Use of a larger diameter needle, avoid over large needle, or an insulated steel needle.

CHAPTER 10

1. Oils extracted from aromatic plants.

2. Smaller.

3. Airtight containers which are made of materials which do not interact physically or chemically with the oil, and protect if from light.

4. Ask your client to check with their homeopath which essential oils should not be used.

5. Spice, flower, tree, resin, herb, citrus.

6. The whole is greater than the sum of the parts.

7. 10 drops.

8. Use less essential oil, less base oil and keep massage shorter and less formal with more stress on lighter movements.

9. The strength and dominance of smell. This may be affected by personal perceptions.

10. Avoid bathing or shower for 8 hours.

CHAPTER 11

1. Always look for the underlying skin tone.

2. The finish will appear raised above the skin.

3. Names of shade numbers of creams used and the proportions used of each. Provide a temporary supply for use until the main supply arrives.

4. Narrow lip brush.

5. Blotting with moist chamois leather.

6. Lowers, withdraws or causes to retract.

7. Artificial appendage.

8. a) Disorders/diseases

   b) Sensitive tissue

   c) Warts/moles

   d) Open skin

   e) Raised blemishes.

9. a) Brush

   b) Sponge

   c) Finger.

10. Highlight outer corners.

CHAPTER 12

1. Radius, Ulna.

2. Keratin

3. The nail root. It is situated below the cuticle and is the living part of the nail containing nerves and blood vessels.

4. To enable accuracy, speed, and effectiveness of treatment. The client will not enjoy the treatment if she is uncomfortable.

5. Damage to the nail plate.

6. Wear gloves as often as possible, especially when cleaning, washing up and gardening.
   Avoid naked flames
   Only use acetone-free enamel remover.
   Always use a base coat to avoid staining of the artificial nail plate.

7. Incorrectly prepared nail
   Incorrect priming
   Not allowing product to remain over the boundaries of the nail.
   Leaving a thick edge near the cuticle.
   Acrylic mixture too dry when applying in the cuticle area.

8. Air bubbles trapped between the nail and tip. Prevent these by carefully squeezing out all the air bubbles, during application to ensure that the tip is flat against the nail surface.

9. Maintenance should be caried out aproximately every two weeks after the initial application.

CHAPTER 13

1. Six precautionary measures to be taken when using heat treatments are

   a) always check for contra indications.

   b) Provide disposable foot wear to avoid cross infection.

   c) Skin test/patch test where necessary e.g. paraffin wax.

   d) Always remain within calling distance of your client/

   e) Ensure the shower area is regularly cleaned.

   f) Move portable lamps and units well away from your client when not in use.

2. Heat treatment will warm the body tissues, making the body more receptive to further electrical treatment hence the results more effective.

3. See page 199.

4. See page 205.

5. Sauna uses dry heat, steam cabinet uses moist heat.
   Sauna is a communal treatment and steam cabinet is more personal.
   Sauna treats the whole body and the steam cabinet excludes the head.
   Steam cabinet is more suitable if your client is slightly claustrophobic.
   Sauna takes longer to warm up to the appropriate temperature.

6. The pulse rate increases and blood pressure falls.

7. See page 199.

8. See page 199.

CHAPTER 14

1. See page 208.

2. See pgae 209.

3. Children are more vulnerable because their skins are less resistant and they burn more easily.

4. See page 208.

5. UVA

6. See pgae 210.

7. Record the reaction on the record card and withdraw the treatment immediately.

8. Carry out a thorough preliminary consultation, patch test the client if you think they may be sensitive, suggest that your client exposes themselves in short doses initially.

16 | Your personal skill check

This section may be photocopied for your continuing personal use, to enable you to evaluate your own development towards competence and to help you to identify existing current competence.

HOW TO USE THE SKILL CHECK

Within the table you will find statements about your job and work activity. In the adjacent columns you tick as you consider appropriate. You should evaluate yourself against all of the aspects of the activity which are indicted. If you never carry out a particular task tick the first column, if you carry out the task but need considerable guidance from your trainer in doing this then tick the second column, if you carry out the task without guidance from others then tick the third column and if the task forms your normal job role or which you carry out on a regular basis you should tick the fourth column. If you intend to claim existing competence or wish to plan how your competence will be assessed, use the evidence identification section to help identify where and how you will produce this.

LEVEL 3 BEAUTY THERAPY

Task	Never done	With assistance	Little assistance	Regularly done	The evidence of competence that I have to support this claim across the range
Respond to enquires about:					
advice and guidance,					
treatment prices,					
range of services,					
range of products,					
complaints,					
Level 3					
Undertake retail sales, including:					
identify customer requirements,					
responding to customer requirements,					
completing the sale,					
sales of cosmetics,					
sales of nail care goods,					
sales of make up,					
sales of perfume.					
Level 3					
Handle returned goods and complaints, including:					
goods in perfect condition,					
goods in unusable condition,					
justified complaints,					
unjustified complaints,					
complaints about retail goods,					
complaints about treatments.					
Level 3					
Provide guidance and supervision of others at work, to include:					
providing guidance in company procedures,					
providing guidance on industry standards,					
plan work activity and use of resources,					
monitor business activity of teams,					
monitor business activity of individuals,					
monitor efficient use of resources,					
monitor safe use of resources,					
providing information to management.					
Level 3					

Task	Never done	With assistance	Little assistance	Regularly done	The evidence of competence that I have to support this claim across the range
Establish contact and respond to your customer's requests during treatment:					
special requests,					
routine requests,					
internal customers (colleagues)					
external customers (clients).					
Level 3					
Provide artificial nail structure, to include:					
preparation,					
application,					
aftercare advice,					
removal,					
ready formed extensions,					
sculptured artificial nails.					
Level 3					
Assess clients for treatments, including :					
oral assessment,					
physical assessment,					
advise on treatment plan.					
Level 3					
Prepare for and provide manual body massage, to include:					
preparation of the work area,					
preparation of the client,					
record keeping,					
evaluation of treatment,					
aftercare advice.					
Level 3					
Prepare for and provide vapour treatment, to include:					
preparation of the treatment plan,					
preparation of the work area,					
preparation of the client,					
record keeping,					
evaluation of treatment,					
aftercare advice.					
Level 3					

Task	Never done	With assistance	Little assistance	Regularly done	The evidence of competence that I have to support this claim across the range
Prepare for and provide high frequency treatment, to include:					
preparation of the treatment plan,					
preparation of the work area,					
preparation of the client,					
record keeping,					
evaluation of treatment,					
aftercare advice.					
Level 3					
Prepare for and provide vacuum suction treatment, to include:					
preparation of the treatment plan,					
preparation of the work area,					
preparation of the client,					
record keeping,					
evaluation of treatment,					
aftercare advice.					
Level 3					
Prepare for and provide neuro muscular electrical stimulation treatment, to include:					
preparation of the treatment plan,					
preparation of the work area,					
preparation of the client,					
record keeping,					
evaluation of treatment,					
aftercare advice.					
Level 3					
Prepare for and provide vibratory treatment, to include:					
preparation of the treatment plan,					
preparation of the work area,					
preparation of the client,					
record keeping,					
evaluation of treatment,					
aftercare advice.					
Level 3					
Prepare for and provide galvanic treatment, to include:					
preparation of the treatment plan,					
preparation of the work area,					

Task	Never done	With assistance	Little assistance	Regularly done	The evidence of competence that I have to support this claim across the range
preparation of the client,					
record keeping,					
evaluation of treatment,					
aftercare advice.					
Level 3					
Prepare for and provide sauna treatment, to include:					
preparation of the treatment plan,					
preparation of the work area,					
preparation of the client,					
record keeping,					
evaluation of treatment,					
aftercare advice.					
Level 3					
Prepare for and provide steam cabinet treatment, to include:					
preparation of the treatment plan,					
preparation of the work area,					
preparation of the client,					
record keeping,					
evaluation of treatment,					
aftercare advice.					
Level 3					
Prepare for and provide spa pool treatment, to include:					
preparation of the treatment plan,					
preparation of the work area,					
preparation of the client,					
record keeping,					
evaluation of treatment,					
aftercare advice.					
Level 3					
Prepare for and provide ultra violet radiation treatment, to include:					
preparation of the treatment plan,					
preparation of the work area,					
preparation of the client,					
record keeping,					
evaluation of treatment,					

Task	Never done	With assistance	Little assistance	Regularly done	The evidence of competence that I have to support this claim across the range
aftercare advice.					
Level 3					
Prepare for and provide infra red radiation treatment, to include:					
preparation of the treatment plan,					
preparation of the work area,					
preparation of the client,					
record keeping,					
evaluation of treatment,					
aftercare advice.					
Level 3					
Provide dietary advice, including:					
establishing current diet,					
planning diet,					
advising on diet.					
Level 3					
Provide individual exercise, including:					
client preparation,					
exercise area preparation,					
provide guidance and advise.					
Level 3					
Provide diathermy needle epilation, short-wave diathermy electrolysis, to include:					
preparation of the treatment plan,					
preparation of the client for the treatment,					
preparation of the treatment room,					
provide the treatment,					
provide aftercare advice.					
Level 3					
Provide diathermy needle epilation, galvanic chemical electrolysis, to include:					
preparation of the treatment plan,					
preparation of the client for the treatment,					
preparation of the treatment room,					
provide the treatment,					
provide aftercare advice.					
Level 3					

Task	Never done	With assistance	Little assistance	Regularly done	The evidence of competence that I have to support this claim across the range
Provide diathermy needle epilation, blend, to include:					
preparation of the treatment plan,					
preparation of the client for the treatment,					
preparation of the treatment room,					
provide the treatment,					
provide aftercare advice.					
Level 3					
Selecting oils for aromatherapy massage, over a range of clients and treatment requirements, including:					
client consultation,					
preparing treatment plans,					
selecting appropriate oils,					
blending oils.					
Level 3					
Providing aromatherapy massage to a variety of clients (with differing needs), including:					
treatment room preparation,					
client preparation,					
treatment,					
evaluate treatment,					
provide aftercare advice,					
maintain treatment records.					
Level 3					
Provide remedial camouflage to a variety of clients (each with differing needs), including:					
preparation of the client,					
producing a treatment plan,					
provide remedial camouflage,					
instructing the client in correct home use.					
Level 3					

Index

Page numbers in italics refer to illustrations or tables separated from their text references.

abdomen
  massage 110–111
  muscles 86–7
acrylic nails 188–91
advice and information 27–8, 36
  in sales 42–3
aftercare
  aromatherapy massage 164
  artificial nail extensions 196
  camouflage make-up 178
  electro-epilation 139
  galvanism 76
  UV treatment 210
  see also homecare advice
age, contra-indicated 84
allergic reactions
  to essential oils 153
  to UV exposure 209
ampoules 74, 75
anaemia, contra-indicated 94
anagen stage (hair) 129, 132
anorexia 93
  contra-indicated 84
antagonist muscles 99
appearance *see* personal appearance
arm
  anatomy and physiology of fore-arm 181–2
  massage 110
  muscles 87

aromatherapist 19–20
aromatherapy massage 148–64
  technique 162–3
  types of client 162–3
artificial nails *see* nail extensions
assessment
  for NVQs 10–11
  of client's treatment needs 28, 29
  see also consultations;
    pre–treatment assessments
asthma, contra-indicated 67, 69, 94, 202,
atrophy onychatropia 184
audio sonic vibrator 118

back
  massage 111–112
  muscles 87–8
Ballet needles 144
base oils 161
beaus lines 184
beautician 19
beauty consultant 20
beauty therapist 18
BIA (Beauty Industry Authority) 10
black pepper (piper nigrum) 154
blend epilation 140–42
blending, nail tips 187
blood pressure, contra-indicated 67, 69, 73, 75, 77, 94, 105, 121, 125, 158, 200, 202, 205, 209
blue nails 184

body language, interpreting, 29, 30, 31
  see also non-verbal communication
body massage 105–113
body temperature 30, 31
body types 91
bones 181–182
bony areas, contra-indicated 72, 75, 77, 116, 125
breasts, structure 88
bruises, application of camouflage makeup 171–2
bruising
  contra–indicated 73, 77, 105, 117, 142, 158, 204
  from vacuum suction 121
bulk packaged products 37
burns, causes 122
business effectiveness, monitoring 32, 38, 41, 45
buttocks, muscles 85
buying signs 42

camomile (chamaemelum nobile) 154
camouflage make-up 167–73
  see also corrective make–up, make–up
cancer, contra-indicated 158
carbohydrates 82
cardio-vascular disorders, contra-indicated 94, 105, 117, 125, 142, 158, 202, 205
cardiovascular fitness 94
career
  opportunities 18–22
  personal action plan 23–5
  professional development 23
Carlton needles 144
cash handling 62–3
catagen stage (hair) 130, 132–3
cellulite treatment 121–2
checking stock, after delivery 53
chemical leakage, stock 54
chemical sterilisation 57

chest, massage 111
children, special treatment requirements 163, 168
clary sage (salvia sclarea) 154
claustrophobia, contra-indicated 67, 200, 202, 209
client care 162
  communication with client 35–6
  barriers 27
  interpreting body language 29, 30, 31
  consideration for elderly 105, 163
  explaining treatments 36, 70, 105, 115, 136, 169, 200, 209
  pre-treatment assessments 28, 29, 66, 91, 136, 157, 167
  responsiveness to client 29
  sensitivity to client 29, 167
  see also clients
client comfort 30, 108, 109, 145, 162
  discomfort caused by prolonged treatment 37
client focus 36
clients
  complaints 39
  confidentiality 28–9, 59, 167, 169
  information for 27–8, 36
  modesty 30, 108, 120
  records *see* treatment records
  sales 28
  treatment plans 31, 66, 115, 158, 168–9, 186
  see also client care
clothing, for therapists 55
colour matching, camouflage therapy 171
communication skills 19, 20, 21, 22
communication with client *see* client care
communication with staff 40
complaints, procedure 39
confidentiality 28–9, 59, 167, 169
conjunctivitis, from UV treatment 209

consultations
  facial electricals 66
  figure postural 91
  interim 76
  see also assessments; pre–treatment assessments
Consumer Protection Act 1987 44
contamination
  in bulk package use 37
  equipment 56
contra-indications 29, 30, 36
  aromatherapy massage 157–8
  camouflage make–up 169
  desincrustation 75
  dieting 84
  electro-epilation 142
  exercise 94
  galvanic body treatments 121–2
  high frequency direct/indirect 69
  infra red light 205
  iontophoresis 74–5
  massage 105
  microcurrent 79
  neuro-muscular electrical stimulation 77, 125
  paraffin wax 204
  sauna 200
  steam treatments 202
  ultra violet treatments 209
  vacuum suction 72–3
  vapour treatment 67
  vibratory massage 116–117, 118
corrective make–up 173–6
  see also camouflage make–up
COSHH (Control of Substances Hazardous to Health Regulations) 49, 54
  assessment 61
costing of treatments 37
cracking, of nail extensions 187
cupping 108
customer service skills 21, 27
customers *see* clients
cuts and abrasions, covering 56
  see also open skin

damaged goods 53

deep terminal hair 131, 132

delivery of stock, checking 52, 53

demonstrator 20

depilatory cream 134–5

dermal papilla 129–30

desincrustation 75–6

desquamation, accelerated from UV exposure 208

diabetes, contra-indicated 69, 73, 75, 122, 124, 142, 202, 205

diet 82–5

dieting, contra-indicated 200

direct high frequency treatment 68–9

disposable covers 38

disposable needles 144

disposal

    electrolysis needles 58

    packaging 53–4

dizziness, contra-indicated 200

doctor approval/referral see GP

dry heat

    sterilisation 58

    treatments

        infra red light 205

        paraffin wax 203–204

        sauna 200–201

dystrophy 184

eau de cologne 110, 112, 120

ectomorph 91

eczema 184

efficiency 36–7

effleurage 107

eggshell nails 184

elderly, consideration for 105, 163

electric shocks 122

electrical equipment, regulations 50

    see also equipment

Electricity at Work Regulations 1989 50

electro-epilation 135–46

electrodes 68, 69, 70, 74, 140

electrologist 19

electrolysis see electro–epilation

electrolysis needles

    storage and disposal 58

    types 143–4

emotional problems, contra-indicated 142

endomorph 91

epilepsy, contra-indicated 73, 75, 77, 79, 105, 117, 122, 125, 142, 202, 209

equipment

    aromatherapy massage 161

    body massage 105

    body treatments 118, 120, 121, 125

    checking 62

    cleaning 56–7

    electro-epilation 136–7

    facial electricals 69, 71, 75, 77, 79

    infra red lamps 205

    iontophoresis 74, 75

    paraffin wax 204

    regulation 50

    safe use of 38, 50

    sauna 201

    steam bath/room 202, 203

    sterilisation 56, 57–8

    ultra violet treatments 209

    vacuum suction 71, 73–4

    vapour treatment 67

erector pili muscle 129

essential oils

    blending 159

    buying 150

    choice 159

    extraction 149

    odour intensity 160

    operation 153

    quantities 160

    storing 150

    structure 150

    types 154–157

    unsafe oils 151–3

    use with homeopathic medication 153

eucalyptus (eucalyptus globulus) 154

evaluation

    of client's needs 31

    of treatments 32, 33, 163–4

    see also monitoring

evidence, for NVQ assessment 10–11

exercise

    controversial exercises 100–101

    effects 97

    for over 50s 101

    in pregnancy and post natal 101

    pre exercise questionnaire 95

    progression and adaptation 98

    safety in 94

    warming up exercises 97

exercise trainer 20–21

eyes

    corrective make–up 173–4

    protection 137, 205, 209, 210

face

    corrective make–up for shape 175–6

    motor points 77

fainting, contra-indicated 200

fake tans 210

faradic stimulation see neuro–muscular electrical stimulation

fat cell count 92

fats 82

feedback

    from client 31–2, 38–9

    to salon staff 32, 40

felon 184

fever, contra-indicated 94, 105, 205

fibre 84

fibreglass nails 191–4

FIFO (first in, first out stock rotation) 53

figure analysis 92–3

fire hazards 50

fire procedures 50–52

First Aid Regulations 1981 50

fitness 94–6
testing 94, 96
flat feet 90
flexibility 94
tests 100
food intolerance, contra-indicated 84
foot
anatomy and physiology 182
muscles 86
fore-arm, anatomy and physiology 181–2
fractures, contra-indicated 105, 158
frankincense (boswelia carteri) 155
frictions 108

GP (doctor)
approval 31, 59, 102, 105, 106, 115, 117, 169, 204
referral from 167
referral to 30, 43
galvanic chemical electrolysis 140
galvanism 74–6, 121–2
gel nails 194–6
geranium (pelargonium graveolens) 155
gyratory vibrator 116–117

HABIA (Hairdressing & Beauty Industry Authority) 10
hacking 108
haemorrhage, recent, contra-indicated 105
hair
bulb 129, 130
growth cycle, 132–4
removal by electrolysis 135–46
removal by temporary methods 134–5
root 129, 130–31
shaft 129
structure 129–31
style for therapists 56
types 131–2

Hairdressing and Beauty Industry Authority 10
hairy areas, contra-indicated 117, 204
hamstring test 100
hand
anatomy and physiology 181
muscles 87
hangnails 184
hazards 50
assessment 61
reducing 53, 54
reporting 38, 50
headaches, contra-indicated 200, 202
health and safety 49
essential oils 151
personal responsibilities 59
records 60
training 60
Health and Safety at Work Act 1974 49
Health and Safety Policy statements 60
healthy diet 82–5
heart disease, contra-indicated 69, 73, 75, 77, 94, 105, 122, 125, 142, 158, 200, 202, 205, 209
heart rate test 96
heat treatments, effect 199
hepatitis B, contra-indicated 105, 142,
heavy percussion 108
HIV, contra-indicated 106
holistic therapist 19
homecare advice
aromatherapy massage 164
body massage 113
electro-epilation 139
NMES 126
see also aftercare
homeopath approval, essential oils treatment 153
hygiene
covering cuts and abrasions 56
hairstyle 56
individual packaging 37

instruments and equipment 56
legislation 48–9, 135–6
in physical examination 30, 168
practice when using bulk products 37
in specialist make–up 168
using make–up 37–8
see also personal hygiene
hyperpigmentation 209
hypersensitivity 43
contra-indicated 67, 72, 75, 205,
hypertrophy onychauxis 184

image of therapist, importance 35, 54–5
indirect high frequency treatment 70–71
individually packaged products 37
inflammable liquids, storage 54, 62
inflammation, contra-indicated 67, 77, 94, 105, 125, 158
infra red light 205
ingrowing nail 184
insulated steel needles 144
insurance 18, 39
interpersonal skills 19, 20, 157, 167
iontophoresis 74–5
IUD, contra-indicated 75, 122, 125

jewellery, removal 56, 71, 74, 77, 117, 120, 200, 205, 210
juniper berry (juniperus communis) 155

keratin 129
keratinisation 132
knock knees 90
koilonc/chia 185
kyphosis 90

laddering 184
lavender (lavendula augustifolia) 155

leconychia 184

leg
  camouflage make-up for veins
    173
  lower, anatomy and physiology
    182
  massage 109–10, 112
  muscles 85, 86

legislation 44–5, 48–50

lemon (citrus limon) 156

lifting
  heavy objects 49, 53
  of nail extensions 186–7

lighting, for camouflage make-up
  170

lips, corrective make–up 176

listening, in consultation 157, 167

Local Government (Miscellaneous
  Provisions) Act 1982 48–9

loose, skin, contra-indicated 73, 116

lordosis 90

lymph nodes 72, 119

make-up
  hygienic application 37–8
  used by therapists 56
  see also camouflage make–up,
    corrective make–up

manager, as role model 35

manicure see nail extensions

manicurist 21

Manual Handling Operations
  Regulations 1992 49

massage
  aromatherapy 148–65
  benefits 105, 106
  body 105–113
  routine 108–112
  vibratory 116–119

meals, heavy, contra-indicated 94,
  202

measurement, from bulk containers
  37

medical history 59, 115

medical records 168

medical supervision, contra-
  indicated 84, 106

medication, contra-indicated 142,
  209

menstruation, contra-indicated 73,
  77, 106, 116, 202

mesophorph 91

metal implants, contra-indicated
  75, 77, 79, 106, 121, 125

microcurrent, electrical stimulation
  79

migraine, contra-indicated 69, 77,
  200, 202

mildew, of nail extensions 187

minerals 84

modesty towels see towels

moist heat
  sterilisation of equipment 58
  treatments 201–203

moles, contra-indicated 106, 117,
  142

monitoring
  business performance 32, 38, 41,
    45
  health and safety 59–60
  ozone levels 67
  security 63
  staff performance 40
  treatments 102, 211
  see also evaluation

motivational skills 21

motor fitness 94

motor points 77, 124

muscle damage, contra-indicated
  77, 125, 158

muscles 85–8
  contraction 98
  flexibility 99
  types of movement 99

muscular endurance 94

muscular strength 94

nail biting 185

nail extensions 186–8
  acrylic 188–91
  aftercare 196
  fibreglass 191–4
  gel 194–5

problem solving and repair 191,
  194
  removing 196

nail tips, application and blending
  187–8

nails
  disorders and diseases 184–5
  functions and structure 182–3

National Standards 10

neck, muscles 87

needles see electrolysis needles

nervous disorders, contra-indicated
  69, 77, 124, 158

neuro-muscular electrical
  stimulation (NMES) 76–8,
  122–6
  comparison with diet and
    exercise 123

non-verbal communication 28, 29,
  136, 157, 162
  see also body language

nose, corrective make–up 174–5

notes (aromatherapy classification)
  159–60

obesity 92
  contra-indicated 84

oedema, contra-indicated 117

onychocryptosis 184

onycholysis 185

onychophagy 185

onychorrhexis 185

open skin, contra-indications 75,
  106, 121, 125, 142, 158, 169,
  204

operations, recent, contra-indicated
  105

overweight, massage requirements
  163

oxygenating cream 70

ozone 66
  monitoring levels 67

pace-maker, contra-indicated 75,
  79, 105, 122, 125, 142

packaging, disposal 53–4

padding for NMES 123
paraffin wax 203–204
paronychia 185
pedicurist 21
pelvic tilt 90
percussion 108
percussion vibrator 118–119
personal appearance of therapist
    29, 35, 54–5
personal career action plan 23–5
personal hygiene 55, 56, 66, 106
    see also hygiene
Personal Protective Equipment at
    Work Act 1992 49
petitgrain (citrus aurantium var
    amara) 156
petrissage 107–8
photosynthesis 150
physical examination 30
picking up (massage) 107–8
pigmentation problems, contra-
    indicated 209
plucking 135
post-natal exercises 101
postiche see wigs
posture 55, 89–91
    defects 90–91
pre-heating
    body areas 71, 120, 125
    of skin, effects 66–7
pre–treatment assessment 29
    body massage 115
    camouflage make–up 167–8
    electro–epilation 136, 137
    essential oils 157
    evaluation 31
    facial electricals 66
    see also consultations; assessments
pregnancy
    contra-indicated 69, 75, 77, 84,
        94, 106, 116, 121, 125, 142,
        158, 200, 202, 205, 209
    exercises 101
premature ageing (skin) from UV
    exposure 208
premises, security 61–2, 63
presentation skills 22

prioritisation of treatment needs 31
prime mover muscles 99
probing 143
product usage 37–8
products, knowledge of 27, 42
professional career development 23
professional indemnity/liability
    insurance 18, 39
progression and adaptation, in
    exercise 98
prosthetics 176–7
    removal in examination 168
proteins 82
Provision and Use of Work
    Equipment Regulations 1992
    50
psoriasis 185
psychological relief, camouflage and
    make–up 178
pteryguim 185

quadriceps test 100
questioning
    for assessment 29–30
    in sales 42, 43
questionnaires 30, 32, 38–9, 95

rays, sterilisation 57
receiving stock 52
reception skills 28
receptionist, knowledge of
    treatments 27
records
    health and safety 60
    stock keeping 54
    consultation and treatment see
        treatment records
re-growth hairs 138, 141, 145–6
remedial camouflage therapist, job
    opportunities 20, 167
Reporting of Injuries Diseases and
    Dangerous Occurrences
    Regulation 1985 50
respiratory disease, contra-indicated
    67, 106, 200,

retail sales person 21
retailing products see sales
    technique
ringworm 185
risk assessment 60–61
root sheaths 129, 130–31
rose (rosa centifolia and rosa
    damascena) 156
rosemary (rosmarinus officinalis)
    156
round shoulders 90

safety
    in exercising 94
    legislation 49–50, 135–6
    working practices 50–1
salaries 19–22
Sale of Goods Act 1979 44
sales technician 21
sales technique 28, 41–4
saline 75, 121
samplers 43
sandalwood (santalum album) 157
saturator electrodes 70
sauna treatments 200–201
scars
    application of camouflage
        make–up 171–2
    contra-indicated 69, 75, 77, 79,
        121, 125, 158, 205
scoliosis 90
security
    of client's belongings 30, 62
    of salon 61–3
    of storage areas 54
sensation loss, contra-indicated 69,
    75, 77, 106, 121, 125,142, 205
shaving 134
shoes, for therapists 55
short wave diathermy electrolysis
    138–9
showering, before treatment 120,
    200, 210
sinus problems, contra-indicated 69
sit and reach flexibility test 100

skin
  disorders/diseases, contra-
    indicated 67, 69, 72, 73, 75,
    77, 79, 105, 117, 142, 158, 200,
    202, 204, 205
  effects of UV exposure 208
  sensitivity tests 75, 77, 115–116,
    121
  types, in electro-epilation 145
  see also loose skin; open skin
skin cancer 209
skin cleansing 66–8
skin fold callipers 92–3
skin rolling 108
skin sensitivity tests 75, 77,
  115–116, 121
SMART performance targets 40
spa pool 203
specialist advice, referral 31
spillages 37, 50, 53, 54
spirit gum 177–8
splinter haemorrhage 185
split nails 185
spoon-shaped nails 185
sprains, contra-indicated 106, 158,
spray activator application
  (fibreglass nails) 192–3
staff
  communication with 40
  monitoring performance 40
staff meetings 40
standards, in good practice 59
steam bath/room 202
steam treatments 201–203
Sterex disposable needles 144
sterilisation 57–8
stock
  checking after delivery 53
  condition and storage 38, 41–2,
    52–3
  handling 52–4
  receiving 52
stock rotation 42, 53, 62
strength tests 96
sugaring 135
sunbathing 210
sunbeds 207, 208

sunblock 210
sunburn 209
  contra-indicated 67, 72, 202
sunlight, rules for safe exposure
  210
sunscreens 210
supervisor
  as role model 35
  matters for referral 29, 38, 39,
    50, 53, 141
  responsibilities 63
Supply of Goods and Services Act
  1982 44–5
swellings, contra-indicated 69, 73,
  158,
synergist muscles 99

talc 70
tanning
  UV treatment 208–10
  inability, contra-indicated 209
tapotement 71, 108
targets, for staff performance 40
tattoos, application of camouflage
  make–up 172–3
tea tree (melaleuca alternifolia)
  157
telogen stage (hair) 130, 133
testers and samplers 43
tinea unguiem 185
towels
  for modesty /warmth 30, 105,
    108, 110, 111, 117, 200
  rolled for support 105, 109, 112
trace elements 84
Trade Descriptions Act 1968 45
treatment plans 31, 115
  aromatherapy massage 158
  camouflage make–up 168–9
  facial electricals 66
  nail extensions 186
treatment records 30, 31, 38,
  59,115, 136, 211
  facial electricals 66
  physical examination 30
  confidentiality 59

treatment room, atmosphere for
  massage 105, 113
treatment times 36–7
  body massage 106

ultra violet exposure, contra-
  indication 67, 69, 202
ultra violet radiation 208–10
  sterilisation of equipment 57
ultra violet tanning treatment
  207–10
underweight 93
Uni probe 145
UV radiation *see* ultra violet
  radiation

vacuum suction 71–4, 119–121
  body strokes 119
  facial strokes 73
  lymph nodes 72
  precautions 121
vapour treatment 66–71
vellus hair 131–2
venthouses and applicators 71
verruca vulgaris 185
vibrations (massage) 108
vibratory massage 116–119
vitamins 83
  vitamin D from UV exposure 208

warming up exercises 97
warts 185
  contra-indicated 75, 106
water 84
wax, re-use 59
waxing 134
whitlow 185
wigs and postiche 177–8
  removal in examination 168
Workplace (Health Safety and
  Welfare) Regulations 1992 49
wringing 108